Encore

Teague Jackson

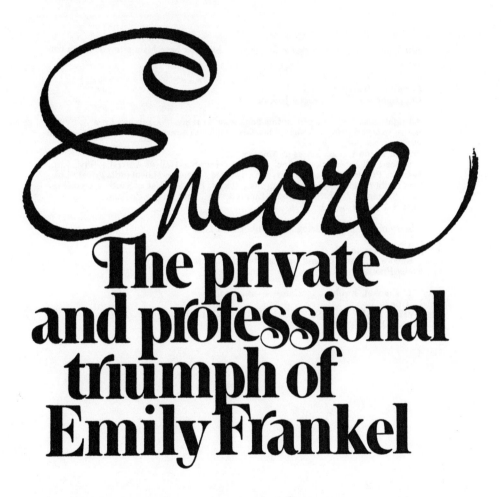

Encore
The private and professional triumph of Emily Frankel

Prentice-Hall, Inc., Englewood Cliffs, New Jersey

Although some of the names and events in this book have been altered, it is a true story.

Encore by Teague Jackson
Copyright © 1978 by Teague Jackson

Printed in the United States of America
Prentice-Hall International, Inc., London / Prentice-Hall of Australia, Pty. Ltd., Sydney / Prentice-Hall of Canada, Ltd., Toronto / Prentice-Hall of India Private Ltd., New Delhi / Prentice-Hall of Japan, Inc., Tokyo / Prentice-Hall of Southeast Asia Pte. Ltd., Singapore / Whitehall Books Limited, Wellington, New Zealand
10 9 8 7 6 5 4 3 2 1

Library of Congress Cataloging in Publication Data

Jackson, Teague.
  Encore : the private and professional triumph of
Emily Frankel.

  1. Frankel, Emily. 2. Dancers—Biography.
I. Title.
GV1785.F74J3   792.8′ 2′ 0924 [B]   78-17259
ISBN 0-13-275032-5

To Emily
A remarkable woman,
who lived it twice

Contents

Encore

1.
Enroute to Indianapolis

Emily stepped to the window, her movements sharp and irritable. It was still snowing, lightly but steadily, over the busy midwestern campus—not enough to stick yet, but enough to turn the barren February ground into a gray slush.

I could always cancel, she thought. Dammit, I just don't want to drive that far in this snow. She pondered the lowering gray clouds. At the very least, the driving conditions would double the time on the road. What if we get stuck in Indianapolis and can't make it back here?

Emily Frankel didn't like snow. It meant damp winter cold that drained the strength from her muscles and joints. Oh, not now, she prayed, not now when I need every possible factor in my favor.

She paced the small hotel room. Years of training and discipline were as much a part of the woman as her long red hair; small, tight, lithe-muscled body; huge hazel eyes in a delicately boned oval face.

1

Because it was her duty, she had agreed to a television interview in Indianapolis, arranged by the Public Relations Department at Purdue. She would be driven by a lady from the department.

Purdue University. Isn't it odd? she mused. Here I am again, for the third time. I don't believe omens; but if I did, I'd have to say it's a good one. My first professional performance, right here, on the same stage. And my first booking. And now tonight. Funny, how destiny has tied me to Purdue.

When the lady gets here, if it looks as bad as it does now, I'll make some excuse, she promised herself. I could really use the rest this afternoon. My Mahler has to be absolutely perfect.

Next weekend, she would premiere the work in New York. The critics were already heralding her "comeback." She smiled at the word, thinking if only they knew how really far away I've been.

I should just reach out, telephone the P.R. Department, and tell them the trip's off. I can make some excuse. Then why *don't* I? Dammit, I wish I wasn't so afraid to just speak out. George told me I simply have to tell people what I think, what I feel.

She rummaged through her wardrobe selecting the outfit for the trip—blue corduroy pants, blue jersey shirt, and black boots. In her white carryall bag she packed clothes for the TV show: the short, clinging lavender jersey dress for the interview. She wouldn't be dancing on the show, so she would have to enchant her Midwest audience with show business chitchat and charm, and discreet display of her good legs and slender dancer's body. Next she chose gray heels, gray panty hose and added a string of antique amber beads, each one double-knotted on heavy-duty thread.

The final item was the chic gray Lord & Taylor coat she loved, with its beautiful silver medallion. Her first extravagance after her husband started bringing home a Broadway star's paycheck, it symbolized New York success, sophistication, and elegance.

Dammit, I'm scared of this snow, she decided. And for once I'm going to say no. She reached for the telephone. It rang before she could pick it up.

"Miss Frankel?" said a bright, cheery voice. "Hi. I'm Claire McKeever from the P.R. Department. You ready for Indianapolis?"

2

"Well, I guess so. But I've been thinking about this weather, and I . . ."

"Oh, it's no problem. Anyway, I'll be driving, so you've got nothing to worry about. I've never had a real accident. The car's outside, all warmed up. I'll meet you in the lobby."

Emily thought, Oh-oh. Too late to cancel now. "Okay, I'll be right down."

As the elevator doors swung open, she was approached by a medium tall, svelte woman with long blond hair worn straight down her back in the currently popular campus style.

The woman announced, "You must be Emily Frankel. I studied your publicity package this morning. Say, those are groovy slacks. And your hair's fantastic. Is it a wig, or is it your own?"

Claire's breezy, flippant air of familiarity was distasteful, particularly her pronunciation of Emily's last name, with the emphasis on the first syllable. In Emily's world, it was pronounced Frank-*el*, giving it an elegant, continental flair. But it was safer to be polite, easier to avoid the risk of hurting Claire's feelings.

The two women turned toward the front door. The snow seemed to be falling heavier. "Are you sure this weather isn't too bad for the trip?" Emily asked.

"No, not at all. I checked the weather forecast this morning and they say by the time we get back, it'll be all gone."

Emily reluctantly shouldered into the bitter wind. As they walked, they left footprints, Claire's small and pointed, Emily's large and square.

Though the heater had been on, the car was chilly, and Emily kept her coat around her shoulders. She opened her carryall and took out the lavender dress, spreading it carefully across the back seat to avoid wrinkles. The beads peeked from the open bag.

Claire edged the car away from the curb. The tires lost their grip for a moment, then regained traction, finally settling into a subdued mushing sound. Claire reached over and clicked the radio to a hard rock station, a spectrum away from Emily's beloved symphonies.

Over the noise, Claire was talking incessantly. "I'll bet you really dig being your own boss. Must be nice not having to punch the old time clock. And to get paid so much money for just one night's work."

3

All people ever saw of her life was on stage, Emily thought. They didn't know of the many weeks spent rehearsing and getting in shape, without a penny of income. They didn't understand that she worked seven days a week, arising each day at seven to get her son off to school, spending six to seven hours in the studio taking barre and perfecting choreography, sandwiching in household duties and preparing dinner for her family, then after dinner returning to do bookkeeping, studying, or planning the next day's schedule. They knew nothing of the dieting, the exercising, the pain, the years she'd spent honing her body.

"Yes," she answered, "It's a nice life. I work pretty hard, but the rewards are worth it."

She didn't want conversation now. Travel time, even on taxis and buses, was the only rest she allowed herself. She needed to relax now, let her mind drift away from her fear of the snow. Besides, as Claire talked, she had the disconcerting habit of taking her eyes from the road to look directly at her passenger. And Claire's right hand was at the bottom of the steering wheel, at six o'clock, and her left at nine o'clock, her elbow resting casually on the door handle.

"Well, I can't really get into dancing myself," Claire answered, again looking away from the road. "But I'll bet it's absolutely fantastic, really far out."

At the entrance to the expressway, Emily could see the few cars on the highway were moving slowly through the storm, giving the snow a better chance to pack down. But good soldiers don't look for excuses. Her father had always said, "Emily, you must always recognize your responsibility, and do it. I will accept nothing less of you." But, if she could get Claire to agree, the cancellation wouldn't be entirely her fault. "Looks like the snow is getting worse. What do you think about turning back?"

"I wouldn't think of it. I told you I've never had an accident, except a few routine bumps and scrapes. I'm like that insurance company, 'You're in good hands with McKeever.' "

As they settled into the rhythm of expressway driving, the speedometer reached 40 mph. Even allowing for the driving conditions, Emily knew they'd left early enough to reach the TV station an hour before air time. "We're not in any rush, are we? I mean, we don't have to hurry to get there?"

"Oh, no," Claire replied. "But I'd rather get there too early, than having to hurry to make it."

4

Her passenger wanted to say, Well, then, why are you hurrying so much now? But that was back-seat driving, definitely a social offense, and so she remained silent.

Claire was chattering away, constantly peering sideways to assess her effect on this VIP entrusted to her care. "Do you have any kids? Sure, you mentioned your son. Well, I'll tell you. Keeping up with those three kids of mine and holding down a job really keeps me hopping."

The conversation was so dull, but the civilized responses were automatic. "No, I don't mind housekeeping. . . . Oh yes, I'm a very good cook. I specialize in Chinese and Hawaiian and I can cook Indian food and Hungarian. . . . No, my husband likes me having a career. . . . Just one child is enough for us. John's an actor. He spends so much time on the road. And my performance schedule has always kept me out of town a lot, too. We don't want a bigger family."

"What kind of place you live in?" Claire asked. "A fancy Park Avenue apartment, right?"

Emily laughed, wishing Claire would keep her eyes on the road. "We're not quite that glamorous, we've got kind of a Bohemian place, I guess you'd call it." She described the four-story loft building, nearly ninety years old. Many years ago, she'd rented the top floor, making it into both studio and living quarters, and filling it with orange crates and Salvation Army furniture.

"About a year ago John and I bought the whole building, so now our apartment is the whole top floor and the third floor is my studio and our offices. We've got more than two thousand square feet on each floor. It's like a ten- or twelve-room house."

"How do you take care of all that space?" Claire asked.

"With a maid once a week, and a half-day baby-sitter/ housekeeper. We do a lot ourselves."

Emily kept a corner of her eye on the speedometer, now registering 45 mph. Claire was keeping plenty of distance behind a brown car with a CB antenna in front of them, but was concentrating more on the conversation than the road.

"You guys own the building. What happens if one of your tenants gets a plugged-up toilet or something?"

"John just goes down to fix it. He's very handy around the house. He wires electrical things, builds things, and takes the garbage out. He even built a floor under our big skylight and hung it on steel beam supports so we could have a desk and a chair up there."

"Imagine that! Your husband a big Broadway star, doing carpentry and fixing toilets. Far out."

The "far out" phrase triggered a dark thought in Emily's mind: I hope he's not out with one of those little would-be actresses. Was he alone when he called me last night? Now wait a minute, she caught herself, that's unhealthy thinking. George taught me how to handle this. Jealousy and fear are my enemies, not John, not other women. George, you're such a good doctor. My dancing was finished, my life was over, and you taught me to believe in myself again.

She tuned back in on Claire's monologue. ". . . but my husband just sat around the house for days, and nobody could get through to him. I wasn't afraid; I saw a shrink. I told the doc all about my husband and the problems he was causing. The doc agreed with me, too. He told me to get a divorce. So I did. Did you ever see a shrink?"

"Hasn't everyone?" Emily answered. But George, you're not a shrink. You *expanded* me. Without your therapy, I probably would have just zeroed out completely.

Up ahead, a gyrating red light jerked her back to the present. On the other side of the road, a state trooper had pulled a car over. "Bunch of crazies out on the road today," Claire complained as they swept past. "Probably going too fast."

Emily sat up straighter. I certainly had some problems when I gave up my company and quit dancing. I was slipping away from reality. Claire would think I was crazy. But George says I wasn't.

What about the death fantasy I described to George—a dead Emily lying there among the candles with hands folded? And not being able to decide what to wear, or how to fix my hair. All those silly lists of household duties I made. That was crazy, wasn't it?

Claire moved to the left lane to pass the brown car. The speedometer needle crept toward 50. The left, passing lane, was untracked, new-fallen snow hiding the ice. If I were driving, Emily thought to herself, I'd stay behind the brown car, no matter how slow he's going. We've got plenty of time.

As they overtook it, the brown car threw slush onto their

windshield. Through the arcs swept by the wiper blades, Emily's eyes resumed their intense stare at the road, willing them safely to Indianapolis. According to the road sign, they had thirty-one miles to go.

She tried for a matter-of-fact tone that would still communicate her fear to Claire: "I guess I'm scared of driving in snow because I've had so many bad experiences."

Claire looked sideways at her passenger. "We're in no danger. I imagine this'll let up any minute now."

Peering straight ahead, Emily said, "I remember one night when I was driving my dance company into Des Moines, Iowa. It was just like today. I was hoping for a let-up in the snow."

"Gee, I've got a cousin lives in Des Moines. Haven't seen her in years. Maybe she saw you dance."

". . . It was just like today, really gray and snowing a lot. I was really, truly, scared. But because I was the driver, and it was my company, I wasn't allowed to show my fear. I had to do my duty. Stay cheerful."

There. I *admitted* I was scared, Emily thought. Claire only nodded attentively.

"We had ten kids in that van. The wind was whipping around, and that van was swaying. Couple times I thought we were going to tip over. And I could hardly see the road. My eyes were burning from staring so hard."

"I can see the road just fine. Anyway, if I can't I've been over it so much I know exactly where it is."

"As I was saying, we had ten kids—three girls and seven boys, gay boys—in that van. And those boys kept moaning about the cold coming in. . . ."

Claire's eyes sparkled. "Is it true that most dancers are queer?"

Emily wished she hadn't started her story, wished she wasn't going to Indianapolis. She wanted to know what time it was, but was afraid to ask, afraid Claire would take her eyes off the road again.

The sign that swept past said twenty-nine miles to Indianapolis.

"No, not most. Most of the girls are straight. A lot of the

guys are gay. But Claire, I was really scared, and I don't mind admitting it. My psychiatrist, George, is always after me to just speak out when something's bothering me, instead of keeping it bottled up inside. He's almost got me convinced he's right."

"You were telling me about the queers—oops, sorry, the gays." Claire said.

"No, not the gays. About the trip into Des Moines. We'd read in the paper that morning about a whole family that froze to death when their car got stuck in a drift on the highway. I was terrified of skidding off the road. It was the kind of conditions where I had to drive absolutely slowly and carefully. Never gun the engine or use the brakes.

"Of course, we finally made it. But I really learned something about myself that day. I suppose that was the incident that finally made me realize that I didn't want to run a company. I was just as afraid as those kids, but I wasn't allowed to show my fear."

The brown car had increased its speed and passed them on the left, its driver grinning over at Claire. Its tires threw wet snow in their path. The arcs of the wipers got narrower as both sides of the windshield built up with snow too cold to melt, too heavy to move. The sound of their tires had changed from the song of pavement to an ominous hush.

"Must be about fifteen miles now, I guess?" Emily asked.

"More like twenty-five," the driver answered.

Emily clasped her hands behind her neck. Her hasty lunch of hamburger and french fries was heavy in her stomach. Why can't I tell her to slow down? She stretched cramped, nervous muscles, tried to return to daily work concerns.

Sorting through her grab bag of problems, she remembered her husband's phone call. He had told her of their son's 102° temperature. I'll call David tonight, she decided. It'll be fun to hear my little Muffin's voice on the phone.

Her stomach felt slightly bloated. Why did I eat that junk food? she asked herself. I should have known better. And this damned weather! Hope my flight home tomorrow isn't canceled. I've got to make that meeting with Maestro Schiff. We've got to go over the tempi.

Thomas Schiff had loved her Mahler. But did it work? The

8

Purdue rehearsal last night had been ragged. And exhausting! A seventy-minute solo *was* exhausting. What would her peers think? What would the critics think?

She crossed her legs Indian-fashion on the seat, stared at her feet, amused at the big, square, funny-looking boots. Well, at least my feet don't hurt.

She uncrossed her legs, returning to the problem. The boots stabbed at the floorboard as she "drove" the car herself, hands clenched and gripping. She strained to see through the frosting windshield.

A billboard flashed by. "See the Museum of Speed— Home of the Indianapolis 500—21 miles."

Emily glanced at the speedometer. Claire was doing close to 55. Again they were closing in on the brown car, its tall antenna whipping in the wind. Maybe if I make a big show of fastening my seat belt, she'll see how really terrified I am. Please God, let her understand and slow down.

As she pulled the belt out of its retractor, she said as calmly as she could, "My husband wouldn't believe this. He's always begging me to fasten my seat belt. I hate the silly things. They're confining. But this snow makes me really frightened." Trying to mute her tone of fear and its implied accusation, she struggled to cinch the belt and catch the stubborn buckle.

Emily jabbered lightly on about why she detested seat belts. On a performance day, it was important to give in to her body's smallest whims; about how difficult it is for a slender person to get a proper fit across the middle; how she hated bunching up her Lord & Taylor coat. Finally, the belt buckle snapped together with a loud click. Can't she see how nervous I am? Why can't I get through to her?

"If it'll make you feel any better, this car has those shoulder belts in the roof, over your right shoulder. Maybe you want to put that one on too."

The speedometer was creeping past the 55 mark, as they drew even closer to the familiar brown car. Am I being punished for something? Emily wondered.

Up ahead, a dark bulk appeared by the side of the road. A car had slid off the pavement and into a snowdrift. The driver waved frantically at them as Claire sped by. "Somebody else will stop. We haven't got time."

Emily glanced out the side window. To their left was the median strip, at least twenty-five feet wide, with no trees, no fence, only a small depression in the center. To their right was an open field with occasional trees, separated from the road by a shallow ditch. We'd be better off sliding into the median, she thought. And if we slid off to the right, we'd be okay as long as we missed those trees.

She squirmed in her seat. Her body tensed, anticipating a blow. An alteration in their car's path jerked her attention back to the moment. Incredibly, Claire was pulling into the passing lane again. They pulled alongside the brown car. Speechless, Emily watched as the brown car gradually accelerated, matching its speed to theirs.

Claire accelerated still more, the car gaining inch by slow inch. Though the speedometer crept past 60, Claire's steady monologue about her son's latest escapade at school didn't slacken. But Emily heard nothing, so intense was her concentration on the race down the cold, snowy road.

At last their car pulled clear, first by a length, then two, then with enough room to pull back to the right lane.

There was an alteration in the tires' sound on the road. The song was gone. Traction was gone. The motion of the car was a smooth glide, then a flat-out skid.

She still had time to observe. Claire's hands were now on the wheel in the proper position. No white knuckles of panic. Attention full on the job at hand. Slight, correct pressure on the accelerator to regain traction. No frantic jabs at the brakes.

Words unsaid, yet meant to be heard, tumbled through her mind. I asked you to slow down. I asked you in every way I could. Why didn't you hear me? She slipped into the attitude she took aboard airplanes; it was out of her hands now; she had done all she could.

The long, lazy drift to the right seemed to go on forever. Emily recalculated: it would be the right shoulder then; perhaps a jar to the right, then a rebound into the path of the brown car. Possibly a roll-over, or escape through the dark line of trees into the white field beyond. In her head, she hummed, "Here . . . we . . . go-o-o," to a nursery-rhyme tune.

10

The car slid over the shoulder, still traveling over 60 mph. It will be the tree, then, she thought, staring at the solid trunk.

Her life didn't flash before her eyes. Straight in her seat, arms at her sides, eyes open and unblinking, Emily Frankel awaited her fate. No plea for help escaped her lips; she didn't fling up an arm to protect her face. She accepted the final blow to her dream. In her last flash of real awareness, she asked herself, why couldn't I tell Claire to slow down?

The car took the impact on the right front, passenger side, as pieces of the wreckage scattered a hundred feet and more.

The seat belt knifed into her lower abdomen. A fraction of a second later, momentum and restraint whip-sawed her torso, tore at her intestine, severed it. Her spine resisted, then yielded, then broke. Except for the seat belt, she would have shot through the windshield and on into eternity. As it was, her face smashed three times into the dashboard, delicate bones shattering with each impact.

The car's engine tore loose from its moorings and crunched backward through the fire wall, pinning her legs against the still forward-moving seat, grinding off her right boot and mangling the foot. Her arms flailed about like the unstrung limbs of a puppet.

Then came the silence, unnatural quiet broken only by the hiss of radiator steam and the final settling of the shattered metal. She would not allow herself to scream or moan.

Three words marched through her consciousness. I am alive. I am alive. I am alive. And I will stay alive, no matter what. I will not die.

Her brain, still on duty, monitored her body's sensations. Adrenaline-rushed, her heart still pumped, but pumped blood through severed flesh. Something wrong with her back, warning her to remain still. Nose and teeth—broken? Something terribly wrong with her stomach. Blood bubbled upward in her throat. Almost gratefully, she vomited over the front of her Lord & Taylor coat.

The driver of the brown car was with them in moments. "Oh, my God! Are you all right in there? Oh, my God. I didn't know . . . I'm sorry." He turned away, masking his own nausea. Turned back to the shattered automobile. "Look, I already called the police on my radio. They're sending an ambulance. You'll be out of there in a few minutes. Can you hang on?"

11

Of course Emily could hang on. But she wasn't sure about Claire, slumped against the twisted steering wheel, her face a bloody mask. "Are you all right, Claire?" Emily muttered. ". . . I . . ." Then, stronger: "I don't seem able to . . . move. I have to dance tonight. I think I'll rest here awhile. . . ." She lay with her face pillowed on what was left of the dashboard, red hair spread out across it.

She glanced down into the footwell of the car and felt revulsion at the sight of her bent black boot, empty, in a pool of blood, dark red and bright. The impact had shot the carryall into the front seat. Her antique beads lay scattered on seat and floor and ground, their double knots and heavy strand broken. A single bead rolled off the seat and fell to the floor.

Her hands, laying palms-up on her knees, were covered with a brackish mess. Surprised, she felt herself crying.

Must check on Claire. Moans were coming from the driver's twisted face, mouth askew and strange. Her hands fumbled at the seat belt. Emily said quietly, "Don't try to move. The worst is over. The ambulance and doctors will be here soon."

But for fifty minutes they lay in the battered interior of the car. Dispatched ambulances stopped at other accidents. A state trooper said later the maximum safe driving speed that day was 30 mph. Waiting, they tried to talk, clinging to life and sanity by the thread of human contact.

Then sirens, coming . . . coming. "I have to dance tonight . . . the lady is coming to iron at five . . . have to lay out bobby pins. . . ."

Hands reached in to cut away the seat belt, the tangled Lord & Taylor coat. "Don't, please don't."

"Lady, we have to get you out," the medic answered.

As he reached in to cradle her in his arms, he could find no recognizable front to her face. He believed she was dying.

She heard someone screaming and it was frightening. She wanted to tell the screaming lady that everything would be all right now. The reassurance struck her funny and she started to laugh.

"She's in shock," one of the men said. Someone took her pulse, expressed despair. She tried to explain, "Don't worry. I have the slow pulse of a distance runner."

The medic sat her up in the back of the ambulance. A rush

12

of pain sent signals to her brain. Before the vehicle could move, she said, strong and clear, "Please wait. My back hurts. George said I should tell you. Maybe you should put me on a board. I have to dance tonight."

Hands lifted her from the bench, laid her on a board. The lady was screaming again. Emily wanted her to stop; wanted to tell her it was okay. But she couldn't find the words.

2.
Indianapolis Hospital

An intern lifted the red blanket. "We've got a Code 99 here," he called. Emily's eyes opened at the sound. Her lips moved.

"What did she say?"

"Sounded like something about wanting to dance tonight," answered the Emergency Room duty nurse.

"Jesus! She's worried about going dancing, and I'm worried about just keeping her alive long enough to figure out what's wrong with her."

Emily's bloodstained fingers plucked at his sleeve. "Right here," she pointed at her abdomen. "It hurts . . . here."

"Okay, lady. Tell me where else it hurts."

"I . . . don't know. Back here . . . in my back. I think something's really wrong with my back. You better . . . X-ray it." The nurse was cutting away her clothes. "Please . . . be careful. Don't move my back."

The intern saw blood still trickling from her mouth. "Internal bleeding. Call Doctor Sam. Get him down here right away."

Hugh Sam, the hospital's resident surgeon, was in the room within minutes. "All right, what do we have here?" The intern and ambulance attendant delivered concise reports. Haltingly, Emily added what she herself knew or sensed.

Sam ordered an injection of pain drug and sedative. "Call Surgery. Get O.R. Three ready for an abdominal resection. Get her blood type. We'll need four pints of whole blood and some plasma too, just in case.

"Is she strapped tight to the table? Keep her immobile; there may be a problem with her back. We can look at that later. Let's get into that stomach or we'll lose her. Could be liver or spleen.

"Have Cook stand by on plastic surgery. As soon as we close, I want her X-rayed. Complete series—head, spine, everything. There may be some other injuries we don't know about yet. And we need permission to operate. Anybody talked to a relative yet?"

"No," answered the nurse, struggling to get a needle into Emily's arm. "She's from New York, but that's all we've got."

He put his face close to the patient's. "Can you hear me?"

"Yes. Please fix me . . . so I can dance."

"Young lady, we're going to see that you get back to dancing and everything else. Now we have to take you to Surgery and we need you to sign the surgical permission form."

"But that means . . . Zephyr can't . . . dance tonight, doesn't it?"

"What the hell did she say?"

The nurse said, "I don't know."

"No. Zephyr . . . She can fly . . . Didn't you know? In the leaves . . ."

"She keeps saying she wants to dance." The intern explained.

"Well, young lady," Sam said. "I don't know anything about any Zephyr, but before you do any dancing, we've got a job to do, you and I."

As John was hurrying down the stairs, he heard the phone ring. The housekeeper called from the upper landing, "It's for you."

He glanced at his friend Glen. "It never fails, does it? People always call when you're in a rush." He yelled back up the stairwell, "I'm late for the theater. Can they leave a message?"

"I don't think so. They said they had to talk to you right away. They said it's an emergency."

"Better go see what it is," Glen said. "I've got my car. I'll drive you to the theater."

He raced back to his apartment two steps at a time and grabbed the phone from the housekeeper's hand.

"John, they just called me from Purdue. Emily's . . . been in a wreck. They—"

"What? Who is this?"

"I'm sorry, this is Sue Ann Mathews. I can't seem to think straight. . . . It's awful, John. I'm so sorry. . . ."

"Oh, my God." He groped backward for a chair, calling for Glen. "Em's been in a wreck. She's hurt. . . ."

Glen took the phone from John's hand. "This is a friend of the family. How serious is it?"

John searched his friend's face for clues as Glen and Sue Ann organized the details. "Okay," Glen finally said. "John will have to get there as soon as possible." He hung up the phone.

"Glen, is she dead?"

"No, but she's in critical condition. There are facial lacerations and internal injuries. They're taking her into Surgery right now. That's hopeful, John. And Emily's a fighter, you know that."

While John grabbed coat, tie, and checkbook, Glen phoned the hospital. They would give no information other than that the surgery was in progress.

Rush-hour traffic to La Guardia was heavy. John missed his flight by six minutes. The next available flight was Allegheny, leaving in fifty minutes.

"You look awful, John. Come on, I'll buy you a drink."

"I don't think I need a drink. What am I going to do? What if—"

"Now stop that. Think positively. That's what Emily would do if it were you."

John answered, "She'd get things organized. That's what I have to do."

17

He bought shaving equipment and had gone to the men's room when he vaguely heard an Allegheny boarding announcement. Shirttail flapping, coat and tie in hand, lather on his face, he ran for the gate. But it was another flight that had been announced.

There was still time for a phone call to Indianapolis. The hospital switchboard operator put John on hold while transferring his call to Surgery. He tapped his fingers irritably while Muzak played in his ear. At last a nurse answered. "The operation is still in progress, sir. I can't tell you her condition. But if she were kin of mine, I'd get here fast."

The two-hour flight seemed to take twice as long. John toyed with his meal, his mind wandering. What'll I do if Em dies? How will I take care of David? Please God, let her be alive when I get there.

He recalled his last words when she was leaving, so happy, so full of life. "Dance well, honey, I'll call you tonight." Were those the last words I'll ever say to her? So trivial. Was that the last chance I'll ever get to tell her I love her—and didn't?

The head of the Purdue Convocation Series picked him up at the airport. "Our P.R. gal was driving the car," the man explained. "I've already talked to Claire. She said the driving conditions were poor—you can see all the snow we've had—and they hit a tree, going about thirty according to Claire. Emily's injuries were caused by the seat belt. . . ."

Seat belt? Emily always refused to wear seat belts. And she's always hated driving in snow. I wonder what really happened? Oh Emily, my poor darling . . .

The hospital, looming medieval and gray against the night sky, was foreboding, isolated in the middle of the snow-covered field.

"Your wife is in critical condition," the nurse in Intensive Care told him. "But she's stable. No visitors are allowed inside now. But the surgeon, Doctor Sam, asked to be notified when you arrived. I imagine he wants to bring you up to date."

The doctors were waiting for John in Sam's office. Hugh Sam was small with black hair, his broad Oriental features creased with fatigue. Dr. Ed Morrison, the hospital's Chief of Surgery, his

18

bushy black eyebrows furrowed, was standing by an X-ray viewer, staring at the film in his hands.

"Your wife's a very strong lady," Sam said. "Dr. Morrison and I were just talking about how lucky she is."

"What do you mean, lucky? She's critical, isn't she?"

"Yes, but we believe she's going to live. Anybody else would probably be dead by now, but your wife will only be crippled."

"Crippled? Won't she be able to dance again?"

"Dance?"

"Yes. She's a dancer, a professional, one of the best."

"So that's what she was talking about in the Emergency Room. Well, let us get to that in a minute. First, let me tell you what we've done so far.

"When they brought her in this afternoon, your wife was suffering from a severed small intestine. Also extensive facial lacerations and multiple cuts and bruises. We removed nineteen inches of the mesocolon in surgery. The operation was successful, and we foresee no complications.

"The plastic surgeon, Dr. Cook, repaired the damage to her face. She has a shattered septum—a broken nose—that is going to give her trouble breathing. There may be some residual paralysis on the left side of her face because of nerve damage. There was extensive tearing around her nose and mouth, requiring seventy-nine stitches to close. Her features will return to normal, though there will be scars. She didn't lose any teeth, but several are quite loose. We had an ophthalmologist check her eyes and he reports massive contusions, but the blood will eventually drain away. There's no evidence of rupture or blindness, though we won't know that for some time."

"But you said 'cripple.' What about that?"

"There are a couple of problems left to solve. Dr. Morrison was briefing me just before you came in."

Morrison held up the X rays. "These show a severe spinal dislocation between the first and second lumbar vertebrae, right at her waist."

"It's just dislocated, not broken, right?" John asked.

"The bones are considerably out of alignment," Morrison continued. "More than two inches, I'd say. And the flanges of the bones are crushed. I rather imagine we'll find considerable nerve damage, but the spinal cord itself seems intact."

"Is her back broken, or not?"

"In layman's terms, yes, it is. But we won't be able to determine the extent of the damage until she regains consciousness. If the nerve trunk, which carries the motor signals from the brain to the lower body, is severed, then she'll be permanently paralyzed below the waist. If there's only partial damage to the spinal cord— which I suspect is the case—then she has the hope of recovering some motor control in the lower extremities."

"Goddamn, what does 'some motor control' mean? I told you she's a professional dancer. That's her life. She'd rather be dead than be in a wheelchair. Isn't there something you can do?"

"Dr. Morrison and I were discussing the possibility of a spinal fusion—if tests show that there is some reasonable chance of her regaining the use of her lower body. Of course, that depends on whether there's damage to the nerve trunk. If there isn't, you can thank your wife's courage."

"What do you mean?"

"She told the ambulance people to put her on a board. If they hadn't, with all those bone splinters, her spinal cord would most certainly have been severed during the trip. I still can't believe that girl managed to stay conscious until she told the attendants what to do."

"But now what happens?" John asked. "Do you operate on her back?"

"That's the other problem I mentioned," Sam answered. "When her intestine ruptured, some undigested food emptied into her abdominal cavity. We cleaned her out as much as we could, but we can't risk operating on her back until we can rule out the possibility of peritoneal infection. She *is* running a fever, and if an infection ever got into her spine, it would be fatal."

John was not prepared for the first sight of his wife in Intensive Care. Emily lay unconscious, strapped to a Stryker bed, machines monitoring her vital signs. Her eyes were closed, the lids purple, dark circles outlining the bone structure. Her cheeks were flushed and swollen. Two tubes were inserted in her nose. One, a catheter, pumped her stomach into a jar half filled with a dark red

20

fluid. The second tube maintained the shape of her nose and enabled her to breathe, though she was rasping air through blood-caked lips and teeth. A metal shield protected her nose, partially covered by small bandages. A two-inch incision below her mouth had been stitched but left uncovered. Beneath the sheet, a catheter emptied her bladder.

John sat by her side, stroking her hands. "I'm here, darling, I'm here," he repeated.

She withdrew her hands and plucked blindly at the strap's buckle, struggling to raise herself from the pillow. John's call was answered by two interns who held her down. A nurse wrapped Emily's wrists in gauze, pinned them to the sheet above her head, then rebuckled the strap.

"Why are you being so cruel to me?" Emily cried. She turned unseeing eyes toward John. "Please untie my hands," she whispered.

"No," John said, as if reasoning with a child. "I can't. It's for your own good."

Her head dropped back against the pillow. She turned away from him, tonelessly echoing, "No."

Emily awoke and saw her husband at her bedside. "What happened to me?"

"You were in an accident. Don't you remember?"

"I thought I dreamed it."

John shook his head.

"Then I won't be dancing tonight at Purdue?"

"The accident was three days ago. You've already missed the Purdue performance."

Missed? Three years of her career had been canceled out, and now this. "How can I do Mahler at Lincoln Center next week without a preview?"

"I'm afraid that's out, too."

She stared at him, her purpled eyes widening and blank. Slowly she turned her head to the wall. Her body grew so still he reached for her wrist. Her skin felt chilled.

"Darling, what's the matter?"

She said nothing. He knew she was disappearing, "zeroing out." She retreated from him, from the physical evidence of her injuries, into that neutral zone where she was safe from the dangerous sense of despair over the loss of Lincoln Center.

After a long silence, she asked calmly, "Why are my hands tied above my head?"

"You were trying to lift yourself up and unbuckle the strap. You can't do that. They don't want you to move."

She glanced from side to side, taking in the web of tubing around her body. She heard the quiet hums and clicks from the electronic machines. It must have been a pretty bad accident, she thought, if I have all this stuff around me. And my body really aches. At least my legs don't hurt, she realized. That's a blessing.

Why *didn't* her legs hurt? Tentatively she tried to move them, but there was no response. She tried to twist her body and jerk free her pinioned hands in order to touch her legs.

"John," she gritted, "un-. . . tie . . . my . . . hands. I won't touch the strap, I promise. Just untie my hands."

He unpinned the gauze wrappings from the sheet. She reached down and felt her legs, realizing there had been no amputation. But she couldn't move below the waist. Not her knees, her ankles, her feet.

"I want to talk to a doctor."

Dr. Morrison, on Grand Rounds with his team of interns, arrived. "I hear I've been summoned. What's the problem?"

"Doctor, I can't move my legs. What's the matter with me?"

"That's what we're here to find out."

He took a pin and feather from his kit, began to run them lightly up and down her legs. He tickled with the feather, lightly pricked her with the pin: left instep, right instep, left ankle, right ankle, calves, thighs, and hips. "Do you feel this? Or this? How about here?"

I don't feel a thing, she thought. But I have to. "Perhaps," she said to Morrison, "I'm not sure, I think I feel it. . . . Right there. Yes, I definitely feel it. See," she added brightly, "I can wiggle my toe. Can't you see? That's good, isn't it?"

He didn't answer. Her toes hadn't moved.

Around the foot of her bed they mumbled words like

22

"fever" and "getting weaker," frowned and mentioned "paraplegia." Safe inside her zeroed zone, she heard the words, but she didn't have to acknowledge them. The group left, but before he was completely out of her room, one intern said, ". . . such fine physical shape, like an athlete. What a shame."

"I'll get out of this bed and I'll march," she called out. "You'll see."

She turned to her husband. "John, I didn't feel anything. But I know I can wiggle my toes."

When the night-shift nurses heard their patient talking feverishly to herself during her sleepless nights, they exchanged worried glances and pursed their lips. Emily spoke in two voices, each one clear and distinct from the other.

"All right, Emily Frankel, I'm tired of hearing you whimper. Watch the clock and don't complain."

"But it moves so slowly. It's so long until my next shot. I can't make it."

"Shut up! You know Frankels aren't allowed to cry like babies. You're brave."

"But I *want* to cry. I *want* to quit."

As the evening hours crept on, the argument intensified; one voice more pitiful and whining, the other tougher, harsher.

"Oh help me. Won't somebody please come help me?"

"Dammit, I told you to be quiet. Have you forgotten that poem, 'In the fell clutch of circumstance, I have not winced or cried aloud.'"

"Sure," she answered herself with bitter sarcasm, "'and my head *is* bloody, but unbowed.'"

Oh, Mother, she cried, what of my beautiful Mahler? I'll never get to do it now. And my little David. Will I ever see you again? Now who will take care of you? I wonder if you'll remember your Mommy. . . .

To help her through the waking hours of pain, Emily created a fantasy she called "Royal Princess." According to the plot, her family ruled a castle filled with jewels and gold, with mother-of-

23

pearl walls and white ivory furniture, with her own royal orchestra and ladies-in-waiting dressed like a royal *corps de ballet*. She, the prima, commanded that there be continuous dancing and playing of great music. But war had interrupted her idyll and she had been cast into this dungeon where she awaited rescue.

The nurses became her jailers. When they came to change her glucose bottle, she startled them by asking, "When do I get my crust of black bread, and something more than this thin cup of gruel?" She identified the doctors and interns as the enemy. Dr. Sam was a kindly counterspy, secretly on her side, while Dr. Morrison was the executioner.

The principal feature of her "cell" was the Stryker bed—the rack in her fantasy. When the interns entered her room every two hours to put her and the bed through its maneuvers, she laughed grimly. "A few more inches today, boys?"

The Stryker bed is a device wherein the patient's body is not moved; the bed itself can be rotated to several positions, including head-over-heels. As they pushed the button starting the rotation, she glared, "Do your worst. I'll never cry out."

Occasionally, in a hurry to get on to another patient, the attendants would forget to move her down to the foot of the bed before beginning the turning procedure. When the bed reached the vertical, head-up position, she would slide excruciatingly downward until her feet jammed into the bottom rail. Though only a matter of an inch or so, this fall caused her abdominal incision to rub against the straps and the awful swelling in her back to rub downward against the mattress.

Toes pointing hard toward the rail, she would reach the vertical, a moment of terror. Mentally she hummed the "Here we go-o-o . . ." nursery-rhyme tune, trying to blot out the anticipation, then the realization of pain, then the fainting dizziness as she pitched forward onto her face.

Finally on the horizontal, she exulted. "I still haven't revealed where the jewels or the gold are. You'll never find out from me."

To support her head, now hanging face down over empty space, they attached an itchy lamb's wool band under her forehead. "Ah-hah," she would murmur, "the Tantalus torture."

To be flipped back again held its own particular fears. A

doughnut-shaped pad of foam rubber had to be placed so that its hole encircled the area of her broken spine. If it were not placed accurately, the pain was intolerable once she was again on her back.

As the attendants left her room, she called a royal challenge, "Farewell, infidels. Long live the Queen."

After the turning of the bed or an injection, she could drift off for a few minutes, free of pain. Only for those brief moments could she release her mind to concerns of home and son and husband. Only then was she really aware of John's presence at her side.

When pain returned, so did she to her zeroed zone. The strategy was to concentrate on the big electric clock on the wall. Watch the second hand, she instructed herself, as it clicks off the minutes. Watch the minute hand, she counseled, as it moves from the 3 to the 4. That's a goal, you can make it. Then watch it go on to the 5.

All right, I'll stand the pain for forty-five minutes, but no more. Then I'll ask the nurses for an extra injection. Forty-four to go. . . . Forty-three to go. . . .

At the forty-five minute goal, she congratulated herself: All right, you made it! Now go for fifteen more minutes. Anybody can do fifteen if they've already done forty-five. . . . At the sixty-minute mark, she would say, I dare you, Emily Frankel. Try another ten minutes. Bet you can't. And she would do it, and then five more, until her strength and resolve could handle the pain no longer. After another injection, she began the routine all over.

"I will not use up my last resource" was another strategy. That last resource might be that extra pain injection, or coaxing nurses and orderlies to talk about themselves, or measuring the room in inches, or counting twigs on the bare tree outside her window, or identifying hospital activities by sound, or calculating in her head on how much it cost to run the hospital—room by room, floor by floor, by the hour, and by the day. As long as there was something left to try, then she could keep on fighting.

The days passed, the battle draining her strength. Not allowed to take food by mouth, other than an occasional sip of broth or water, she was losing weight, down to 95 from her normal 110.

One night someone, she never found out who, called for the hospital chaplain. In the midst of her nightly two-voiced dialogue, he approached her bed and touched her hand. "It's all right, sister. I'm here to make it easier for you. Do you have anything you wish to confess, anything to say . . .?"

Numbly, she stared at him.

"You don't have to be afraid anymore. Soon you can rest in the hand of God." He unpacked his ritual equipment—white cloth, vial of holy water, Bible, and stood over her, murmuring prayers.

Suddenly she understood the purpose of his visit. "No," she said, tight-lipped and calm. "No. Please leave. Leave me alone. I don't need you."

After he was gone, she spoke out loud: "God, if I'm going to die, that's okay, if that's what you want. But *I* don't want to die. And if I don't, I vow to you again that I am going to dance."

"We have to go ahead with the fusion," Sam argued with his chief, "or it's going to be too late. It may be too late already."

"I think you're letting your personal feelings outweigh your professional judgment," Morrison answered. "As long as her fever persists, there's the possibility of peritonitis, and the surgery involves too much risk. Of course we can't know until we get in there, but the tests show no evidence of healthy nerve tissue, and she's weakening every day. I simply can't take chances."

Sam said. "I know she'd play the long shot. She's told me that if she can't dance again, she'd just as soon be dead. I believe her. She's not afraid of death."

"I understand how you feel about this girl, Sam, but the answer's still no. Unless and until we can solve the fever, I must withhold permission."

Sam sighed. "Let's try her on tetracycline. It's a nonspecific. Who knows? Maybe we'll—she'll—get lucky."

The tetracycline seemed to work. Her temperature returned to normal. Sam phoned Morrison, "I was right, Ed. Her fever's broken. I believe we can rule out peritonitis."

The operation was scheduled. John flew in to be at his wife's side. He had been commuting—half a week in New York with his son and his job, the other half in Indianapolis.

"I'm going to be up and out of this damn contraption," she began as soon as she saw him. "I'm going to walk again. I'm going to dance again." She was full of plans, more animated than at any time since the accident. "I'm going to work so hard in physical therapy. I'll bet I'll be walking, at least on crutches, when I get home.

"Who do you think we should invite to a homecoming party? Let's order a case of champagne. And get a big cake. It'll be better than opening night at Sardi's."

John interrupted, laughing, "And you know what David did when he heard me talking about this on the phone? He started practicing a 'Welcome Home, Mommy' song. He made it up himself."

Emily called for a nurse to bring her a comb, brush, and some ribbons for her hair. "You know," she joked, "I've spent years trying to keep my weight down. And all I had to do was come here. I must have lost fifteen pounds, at least. I'm going to recommend your institution to all my friends."

But in the morning, Dr. Morrison walked into the room, looking unusually serious.

"Well," she greeted him, "you certainly don't look very cheerful for my biggest day here. Are you going to describe the operation to me? Then start prepping me?"

"No. I'm afraid there won't be any operation. Your temperature went back up this morning. Apparently the tetracycline hasn't been completely effective. We're postponing the surgery."

The doctor left. Emily lay silent, her eyes closed.

"I know what a blow this is," John persisted. "It's a blow to me, too. But we've got to talk about it."

"Why?"

"Because we both know what canceling the operation means, and we both have to be able to talk it out, get it out in the open."

She shook her head. "There's nothing to say."

"Yes. We can figure something out. This isn't the end."

"Oh?" she laughed bitterly. "If I can't dance, it is."

"There are other things you can do. You can choreograph. That's one of your greatest talents."

"A choreographer in a wheelchair? Let's just drop it,

27

okay? I don't want to talk about it." She was rubbing an inflamed spot on her arm. "Dammit, this sore is still bothering me. What does it look like to you?"

He glanced quickly, shook his head. "Em, several producers have asked you to choreograph Broadway musicals."

"No. I mean really look at it. It feels warm. Does it feel warm to you?"

"Em, stop fiddling with your arm and concentrate on what I'm saying, please."

"You know," she mused, remembering. "That nurse in Emergency, when I was brought in . . . I seem to remember she had a lot of trouble getting a needle in my arm. Right here, on this spot. She had to stick it in a couple times, twist it around a little. Do you think *this* might be causing the fever?"

The incident was reported, a new pill prescribed, and the mystery of the stubborn fever was solved.

The evening before the operation, Dr. Sam came to her bed for his final examination. Emily held out a handful of letters she had received from New York. "Look at these. I'm going to dance again. Everybody says so."

Maestro Schiff, conductor for her Mahler performance at Lincoln Center, sent a telegram: "YOU ARE A GREAT DANCER AND A GREAT WOMAN. I AM LOOKING FORWARD TO WORKING WITH YOU IN THE FUTURE." Sue Ann Mathews wrote, "You're not through. You're only temporarily out of commission. Yesterday, a representative of the State Department called asking when you'd be available for a South American tour. And the Festival of Cologne wants to book you for next summer. And we've got a nibble from the Festival of Two Worlds in Spoleto."

Dr. Sam laid the letters aside and concentrated on her charts. "I will dance again, won't I, Dr. Sam?"

His "Hmnnn . . ." was the only response she could elicit.

She tried another tack. "Tell me about my recovery period."

"You'll probably be in a cast for at least six months. Then it will be another six months or so in a wheelchair and on crutches. Then, maybe, you can try to learn to walk again."

Hearing only what she wanted to hear, she thought, six months. And six more. That adds up to a year. I can dance again in a year.

"Doctor, I quit dancing for three years and got it all back. So a year isn't too bad. And if I work really hard in physical therapy, I can dance before the year is up. In fact, I'll bet I'm back dancing before twelve months."

"I don't think it's a matter for betting, Emily," he answered. "For now, let's just get through tomorrow."

Get through tomorrow. Get through tomorrow. George told me to work through each day as it comes. Get through tomorrow. In her mind, the nursery rhyme was starting again: Here . . . we . . . go. . . .

3.
Manhattan:
The Year Before

"Sorry," Emily said to George. "I'm just a little tense, I guess. I don't know what's supposed to happen."

"There's nothing very formal or structured here," the psychiatrist answered. "Just sit wherever you feel most comfortable. Personally, I recommend that recliner."

It was a big, deep chair, covered with a nubby, dark green fabric. There was a gold throw pillow for nervous hands. She perched on the front six inches of the chair, her back held willfully straight. "Now what happens?"

"We just talk. Perhaps you'd like to tell me why you called yesterday."

She nestled back in the big chair. It *was* comforting and protective. And the footrest popped up just like he said it would. The fabric, gentle to the touch, was full of the odor of pipe tobacco. She noted the rack of pipes on his desk. It was definitely a "Daddy chair," like the one her father used to sit in when she was a little girl.

31

"Aren't you going to give me some tests before I start talking? Have me look at pictures of ink blots, you know, Rorschachs? Or give me a battery of profile tests with all those questions that relate to each other so you can catch me in a lie?"

"I'm not going to give you any of those, at least not now. Maybe later, if I decide they're indicated. For the time being, let's just chat."

He didn't look at all Freudian, she thought; rather the opposite, in fact. A small man, almost colorless, even mousy, with a bulky turtleneck sweater that failed to hide a slight paunch. She waited for a clue, but the doctor simply sat there, silent.

"What do you want to talk about?"

"It's not what *I* want to talk about. It's what you want to talk about. We don't have to talk about anything you don't want to. What we *do* have to learn is to not sweep anything under the rug."

"I'm not sweeping *anything* under the rug," she flared.

"You seemed disturbed when you called me yesterday. You want to talk about that, Miss Frankel?"

"Just to start talking at random seems so silly. I mean, I don't know where to start."

"Maybe you'd like to start at the beginning, if that's easier for you."

"You mean chronologically?"

"Whatever comes into your mind."

Maybe I should tell the doctor about my dreams. Isn't that what analysts usually talk about? Or maybe he wants to hear about my father.

"I suppose I could tell you about my father, or music, or Zephyr."

"Zephyr? Who is Zephyr?" His light gray eyes lifted from his note pad and fastened on her.

"Well . . ." Emily started hesitantly, "*I* was Zephyr. I had a wonderful imagination when I was a child." Those were the days when she would lie at her father's feet, pretending she was part of the pattern in the Oriental rug. Her father used to sit in his big chair, reading the newspaper and listening to the music while she dreamed of Zephyr. ". . . Zephyr was a picture in a book I stole from my oldest sister's special shelf. The *Snip-Snops* book. She was

32

the most beautiful creature I'd ever seen, and she was flying. No, soaring."

Emily waited for the doctor to respond. But all he said was "Yes?"

"She was everything I wanted to be, but wasn't. I had freckles. I was skinny. And I was the smartest girl in school, a bookworm, and not popular with the boys. She was beautiful. And she had on a peach-pink gown that floated around her, not hand-me-down clothes like mine. And long golden hair streaming out behind her like rays of the sun. I had red hair that Mama always braided into stiff pigtail loops. Her feet were in pink satin slippers and she was floating over rolling green hills covered with budding dogwoods and daisies. Zephyr was spring, flowers, and chiffon. Delicate and queenly . . . and so graceful." Emily felt herself about to cry, then caught herself. No, I mustn't, not here, in front of this man. That's so undignified. "Anyway, more than anything in the world I wanted to be Zephyr. And look at me now. I mean, I thought about Zephyr yesterday, and. . . ."

The psychiatrist reached for a box of Kleenex on his desk. Two more boxes were prominent in the room. She wondered how many other women had cried in this room, sitting right in this chair. But I don't want to be like his other patients.

She waved away his offer of a tissue. "Okay. So that's my crazy Zephyr story. I still believe I'm Zephyr. Or did. But that's why I'm here, isn't it, Doctor? Because I'm crazy?"

"I don't think you're crazy. Do *you* think you're crazy?"

"Well, I know what's real and what's not. What else do you want to hear about?"

"You mentioned yesterday . . .?"

"I don't want to talk about yesterday. Not now." It was safer to keep talking about her childhood. "Should I tell you about my father?"

"Certainly, if that's what you want."

"Yes. That's what I want. My father was a wonderful man. . . ." She picked the adjective carefully. I don't want this psychiatrist blaming my problems on Daddy; it's not his fault. "He would sit in his great big chair, just like this one, and listen to records of all the great composers.

"Through the windows I could see our huge maple tree, the kind you can sit under in the summertime in the cool shade while you eat a Popsicle and read a book. The sun shining through the leaves making shadow patterns on the rug, me lying on the floor at Daddy's feet, becoming part of the rug pattern, then getting up and trying to place my feet on the shadows and rug patterns in time to the music. I felt I was magic, doing real dance steps, a minuet."

This time, when the doctor proffered a tissue, she was crying openly. "I'm afraid my mascara's running. I must look a mess. I'm sorry. . . ."

What an odd little man he was, not at all what she'd expected. He seems almost boyish. I thought he'd be very Freudian, formal and theoretical. But he's not, he's nice. I hope he doesn't think I'm just another crazy lady. . . .

Again Emily utilized only the front six inches of the recliner chair. Her resolve was as rigid as her back. Now, she promised herself, I will not keep on jabbering. "You just sit there and listen. When do *you* talk?"

"Later, maybe," he laughed. "That's the way analysis works."

"But aren't you supposed to give me things to think about before my next appointment?"

"Sure, I can do that later, after I know more about you. You wouldn't want a doctor prescribing medication until he had your medical history and an exact diagnosis, would you, Miss Frankel?" He sat silently, watching her.

I know what he's doing, she thought. He's playing the silent game with me. He won't say anything until I say something. Well, I can play that game as well as he can. I'll sit here and wait. I'm sure he wants to know why I called him yesterday, but I wish *he'd* bring it up. It'd be easier to talk if he'd ask me questions.

"You know," she said finally, "you look just like my father when you smile like that. Daddy would smile that way whenever my sisters and I said something he thought was particularly smart or pertinent. Intellectual conversations with Daddy were a big deal in our house, at least for me. It was my way of getting his attention. He loved me when I asked him about grown-up things, like, 'How do car engines work?' and, 'How did things go at the office today?'"

Emily relaxed into the big chair, remembering conversa-

34

tions about complex business negotiations, employees Daddy had hired or fired. He talked to her like an adult, about machines that had broken down and needed replacement. "He was in the children's dress business. He owned the company. Some of my happiest memories as a child were when he'd take me to his factory on Saturdays. While he worked in his office, I'd wander the aisles on the floor, touching and smelling the bolts of fabric, the colors and patterns. And men would come up to him and speak so respectfully. He'd be so polite, cool, and formal. In the family, too, he was the king. We all orbited around him. And Daddy used very big words, so of course I learned all the big words I could."

That's what Daddy loved in me—my brain, she thought. I'd talk about things he wanted to hear. My sisters and I competed for Daddy's attention. That's how I won.

"One of the big words we girls used was 'self-abnegation.' That was Daddy's word for my mother." She considered her next words carefully. "Mama was entirely different from Daddy. She was a tough kid from the Lower East Side. And when she met Daddy, she surrendered everything that was her—her dreams and goals— to him. He was everything she'd ever wanted in a man—intellectual, fine manners, moderately well-off. She was proud of him, his position, the way he dressed. She insisted that he always have ten starched white shirts hanging in his closet. Even though we had a live-in maid, Mama would do the shirts herself. She was always washing and ironing. She slaved for Daddy, and we girls hated her self-abnegation."

"You said, 'we girls,'" the doctor said. "How many were you?"

"Three." It was a wonderful family, she reminisced. Really together. "We Frankels," we used to say, and take joy in how much better we were than anybody else in Harrisburg.

Then what happened? Why did everything go wrong? Why did I stop being a winner? Maybe Daddy was right in his prediction.

"Do you think that's what went wrong with me?" she appealed to the doctor. "So much competition?"

He glanced at her, but didn't say anything.

"Well? What's your reaction to that?" she challenged.

"What's *your* reaction to that?"

"I want to know what *your* reaction is. I don't care about my reaction. Why don't you ever say anything? I think you're trying to trap me."

"Is there a trap?"

"I don't know. I don't want to talk anymore."

"Okay."

She sat in stubborn silence. Finally the first session was over, and she grabbed her purse and got up to leave. "I don't know if I'll see you tomorrow or not."

"Well, I'll hold your time open, in case you decide to come."

A big Checker cab picked her up outside the psychiatrist's office. She liked the old Checkers; she could stretch her legs. "Nice day, isn't it?" the driver chattered on about the weather, the city, people in general. How delightful to have somebody else do the talking, she thought. I hadn't realized how exhausting it is to talk nonstop for almost an hour.

The car swerved sharply as another taxi cut them off at a light. Angrily, rolling down his window, her driver spewed invective at the offending car.

I wish I could be like that, Emily thought. He's learned not to sweep things under the rug, like the doctor advised me to do. He's probably right—it *would* be a lot better for me to just let it all out.

Back home, she again felt the oppressive lassitude of the previous weeks. Out loud she spoke: "I wish John would call." But there was no answer from the empty room. The phone hadn't rung in two days.

And she wasn't going to call him. He'd be out, and then she'd start imagining all sorts of things. How can he resist those aggressive women? I wouldn't resist, either, if I were he, with a depressed wife like me waiting back home, crazy, nonfunctioning. It's time he went on without me. He'd have a better career if I weren't around for him to worry about. She tried to read a book, but her mind couldn't concentrate beyond the second page. Hoping for a rare night of sleep, she went to bed early, taking two pills instead of one. Sleep refused to come. Nothing's changed, she decided. Everything's still as awful and empty as it was yesterday. The doctor didn't give me anything to hang on to. Just talk, my talk. Should I go back?

36

"Good afternoon, Miss Frankel."

"Hi, Doctor. I feel like I'm beginning to make some progress. It's taken me a couple weeks, but I'm starting to understand why you keep telling me to not be afraid of expressing my feelings straight out. To start with, I wish you wouldn't call me 'Miss Frankel.' I'd be more comfortable with 'Emily.' "

"Okay, Emily, if that's what you prefer."

"And," she added, "I hate calling you 'Doctor.' It seems so impersonal. What do your other patients call you?"

He smiled encouragingly. "My friends call me George."

Isn't it funny how he smiles? she asked herself. Most people's eyes get narrow when they smile. His eyes get wide and really project something warm. His eyes look like Richard's. They're so light colored, they even look like John's, the way they almost disappear. Burton and John almost have the same eyes.

That night in our studio when they just kept pouring down the liquor, Richard the vodka and John the Scotch, and they got louder and louder. I was afraid they were going to wake up the whole neighborhood. Then they'd gone out barhopping. Hours and hours. I lay in bed and listened in fear, praying for John's footsteps on the stairs. Then I went to the window and watched the streets. I counted taxicabs, told myself he'd be in the seventh one. But the seventh cab always went on by without stopping.

Suddenly she was aware of George sitting there patiently, watching her. "All of a sudden I feel so blue. I don't know what's the matter with me. I came in here feeling positive, but now. . . .

"My life has been so awful and empty lately. I used to be able to handle the bad things with just my own determination. I remember after I'd begun dancing professionally, my father told me again that he didn't approve."

George's eyebrows raised quizzically. "You hadn't mentioned before that you're a dancer."

"I guess I forgot to tell you. I suppose you thought I was just an ordinary housewife, didn't you? But I'm a dancer. That's my profession, or at least it used to be. That's part of the problem, part of why I'm here. . . ." She stopped, then continued, "You see, Daddy never thought dancing was a proper ambition for a Frankel. When I was little he tried to stop me.

"Lots of times my parents had callers on Sunday afternoons, and Mama and Daddy were always showing us off. My sister Sara would play the piano and sing, Debra would turn the pages of the music book.

"I wanted to dance for the visitors, but Daddy made me recite 'Invictus': 'Out of the night that covers me, / Black as the pit from pole to pole'—I always lowered my voice dramatically for the next part—'I thank whatever gods there be / For my unconquerable soul.' It was his favorite poem.

"One afternoon, when Daddy was at work, I got to dance for a friend of my mother's. Afterward, I eavesdropped and heard what the lady said: 'She reminds me of the great Pavlova. Emily has grace, and a sublime sense of the music.' I couldn't wait to tell my father. I was sure he would be impressed, and then he'd let me take lessons. But he said, 'Emily, you have much too fine a brain to waste it on something like dancing. You should think of being something more important, a professor in a university, a doctor, or a lawyer.'

"I told him that dancers could be important too. But he told me, 'It's fine to want to be famous. And I'm certain that as you grow older, you will find other famous people you'll want to emulate. So I will make you this bargain: If, when you graduate from high school, you still wish to learn to dance, then I will pay for your lessons.'

"But I was eight years old and I knew I couldn't afford to wait that long. I'd read lots of biographies in the library and I knew that dancers all started before they were eleven or twelve. It seemed to me that the people who succeeded in life were the ones who never gave up their dreams. Here Daddy was telling me in effect to give up my dream of dancing. He'd given up his own dreams—that was what was so confusing and painful to me."

"Oh?"

"Yes, he'd given up. Daddy always wanted to write a book. Maybe because my grandfather, Grospapa Frankel—he was an Orthodox Rabbi—had written translations of ancient Hebrew. Daddy was going to write about Felix Adler and philosophy, but he never got beyond the talking stage. He even built a study so he could write. But all he ever did was go in there after dinner, read his paper for ten minutes, and fall asleep.

38

"My mother, when *she* was a little girl, dreamed of being a dancer too. But she became a housewife. Every morning she'd get up at six-thirty to get us ready for school. Then she fixed Daddy's breakfast and started cleaning the house, every day, even though we had a live-in maid. She did the grocery shopping and even after dinner she didn't rest. She'd go and do the dishes and the ironing and the family bookkeeping.

"I knew I never wanted her life of 'self-abnegation.' I swore I wasn't going to be like that, George. I wasn't ever going to give up my dream. And now—" She reached for the box and took out a handful of tissues.

"Look at me, I'm a failure, just like they were. . . . No, dammit, they *weren't* failures, really. My mother was a *good* housewife. But not me. I can't even organize my days. I can't do anything anymore. And my beautiful dancing, it's all gone. . . . Have I lost it forever?" She crumpled the Kleenex, tried to stuff the soggy remainders in her purse.

"What do *you* think?" George answered quietly.

"Is that just another of your psychiatrist's tricks? What am I paying you all this money for anyway?"

"No, it's not a 'psychiatrist's trick' as you call it. But your time is up, I'm afraid. We'll go on with this tomorrow, if you like."

"Well, I don't like." She gathered up her things and stalked out of the office.

She arrived at his office twenty-two minutes early and sat fidgeting until the door finally opened. "I'm sorry for my outburst yesterday, George. Please accept my apology. You were only doing your job."

Instead of sitting behind his desk, George took the massive leather armchair beside the recliner, with only a small lamp table between. He sank back with a sigh, his small frame nearly swallowed by the wings of the chair, and opened his notebook on his lap.

"I was wrong, wasn't I? I suppose you think the anger was good for me, don't you? Isn't that what all psychiatrists want? Well? Well, I guess it worked. . . ."

"Oh?"

"Yes. Last night. I put on some records, and that's the first

39

time in a year I've really been able to listen to music. John's staying out on Long Island in a show. So I just sat all by myself in that big room that used to be my studio and listened to Beethoven.

"I was thinking about my father again. I had figured out a plan so that he'd have to let me take dance lessons. I wrote him a letter—very formal, very correct. In it, I promised to drink four glasses of milk every day, go to bed every night at nine-thirty, clear the table and wash the dinner dishes every night, and clean up my room three times a week—all for three months—and do errands for the neighbors to earn enough money to pay for dance school myself.

"Daddy gave in—I guess he appreciated my business-like way of asking and my planning. I knew he would. Those three months—I did everything I'd promised in the letter. . . ." She thought a moment, took a deep breath. "Well, I really didn't do *all* the things. I cheated. I hated milk so I'd rinse out a clean glass, then show it as proof that I was conscientious about cleaning up after myself, too. Or I'd simply pour the milk down the drain, or out the window. And I'd go to bed at nine-thirty every night, but not necessarily to sleep. I'd get under the covers and read with a flashlight." So anyway, I finally enrolled at the Laurelton School for Dance. It was the best school in Harrisburg. I was nine years old.

"The evening before my first class, I picked out my outfit. It seemed to me that dance class would be like gym class at school, so I picked out my green gym bloomers. And of course I took my toe shoes—ballet slippers with hard toes so you can dance on point. I'd saved up my allowances and bought them. The day I got them I remember sitting cross-legged at my shrine and—"

"What shrine?" he asked.

"There was a sacred corner of my room. I had pictures of famous dancers clipped from *Dance Magazine* and taped to the wall. I had a mail-order barre, too, that the maid helped me install. And that day I got the shoes—how carefully I unwrapped that tissue paper. The pink satin was so rich to the touch. They had an odor, a blend of satin, glue, and wood. At first I just turned them over and over in my hands, bending the arches. Finally I put them on, crisscrossing the ribbons around my ankles." She paused, dreaming. "Anyway, the next day I was off to dance school. That's where the fun ended.

"Miss Charlotte Laurelton was the first real live dancer I'd ever seen. I had expected some sort of composite of Nana Gollner, Maria Tallchief, Ulanova, and Slavenska. And there she was, a lumpy

40

woman in a too-tight leotard, glasses, straggling gray hair in a bun. She hardly said anything—took my money, motioned me through a curtain into the dressing room. Another disappointment—narrow little room, little girls taking off their clothes and trying to hide their nudity, dumping their clothes in piles on the floor. There weren't any hangers, not even hooks. And the smell of those sweating bodies in a cramped space. I was putting on my toe shoes when Miss Charlotte walked through and saw me. 'Oh, you won't be needing those, dearie,' she said. 'Not for your first class.' I asked her what I was supposed to dance in. 'Well, if you don't have proper ballet slippers,' she sniffed, 'I suppose you'll have to take class in your bare feet.' So I hid the toe shoes under my clothes and walked into the studio barefoot.

"It was awful, that first day in class. There was a girl standing next to me: long blond hair with pink ribbons, slender, nail polish, sassy little ruffled skirt. The other little girls in pretty leotards or tights, some even in tutus. I can still see myself in that full-length mirror across the studio—knobby knees, my stiff pigtail-looped hair, big bare feet, and green gym bloomers.

"I had no idea what to do. Nobody pays any attention to beginners in dance class. You're just supposed to watch what the others do and try to copy. Miss Charlotte was saying French words I'd read in books, but I had no idea how they sounded when spoken aloud. They ran through the exercises at the barre in all five positions, but I didn't even know how to get to the first position. By the time I'd figured out how to do 'first,' everybody'd gone through 'à la seconde' and 'third.' Then they had an exercise where you had to run across the room and jump. My feet got tangled up and I fell down. Everybody laughed.

"As soon as class was over, I tried to get ahead of the other girls so I wouldn't have to face them. I just threw my coat over what I had on and grabbed up my bundle of clothes. That's when I found my toe shoes were gone. All Miss Charlotte said was, 'That's too bad, dearie. You should have left them at the front desk for safekeeping.'

"I cried all the way home. Debra and Sara teased me. I went up to my room, cried some more. Thought about Zephyr and sat there, looking at the dancers' pictures. I think that's the first time I ever disappeared."

"Disappeared?" George asked.

"Went into neutral. I had a refuge in my mind where

nothing could get in but what I allowed in. That way I could rest and shut out all the pain and humiliation and just hear music and see rug patterns. Then I started to solve the problem. First thing was to go back to my chores, earn money, and save to buy proper dance clothes and a new pair of toe shoes. Second thing—get a French dance book and learn the phrases and movements. That's what I always do when I get in trouble. I tackle the whole problem by breaking it into small parts, then attack each part.

"By the time I went back to Miss Charlotte's class, I was like everybody else—I knew what they knew. I'd caught up. And I conquered class by doing twice as much as any other student. I didn't just study the French ballet book I bought, I practiced at home every day and took notes. When I'd come home from dance class, I'd write down the whole routine and the corrections Miss Charlotte gave me. And the other girls' corrections, too.

"There are things in dance class that the books and teachers don't show you. The dressing room, for instance. There's protocol to be observed. I've seen it in every studio dressing room I've been to. You take your clothes off very nonchalantly, like it's the easiest thing in the world. But you hide your body. You're never blatantly naked. Dancers are very competitive and jealous of other dancers. They're always checking to see who has the longest legs, most slender waist, most delicate chest—dancers don't want large bosoms—smallest, most boyish hips; neatest hairdo; best classic profile; longest neck; and most of all, the pointiest feet."

She paused, hoping for a comment from George—maybe a compliment on her good legs and slender figure. With the depression of the past months, it would have been nice to hear one. The look in George's eyes seemed complimentary, but he was silent, as usual.

"In the class itself, there are more survival tricks. It's the same in every dance class I've ever been in. Even when you haven't the slightest idea what's going on, you learn how to look good, absolutely confident and secure. It's an air of assurance, of being on top of everything—'command of the stage,' it's called. That's one of the things my reputation used to be based on—my power and confidence on stage.

"I think every young dancer learns early on to imitate the best girl in class. At Laurelton I placed myself near the best girl, watched her out of the corner of my eye and in the mirror. And, of course, there's something to be careful of there, too. You've got to be near enough to the best girl to be able to see her, yet far enough from her so that you won't look bad in comparison.

"Then there's the scramble, the race for position, that goes on in dance class. You don't want to be first in line at the barre, because you've got nobody to follow. After the barre, there's another skirmish for center work. You have to get across from a 'thin' mirror, not a 'fat' one. It's the curvature of the glass. Some mirrors make you look fat. Dancers are always dieting—the best weight for a dancer is about ten pounds less than her frame requires. So you've got to get a thin mirror. It's a matter of morale. A dancer has to love the way she looks. She has to *know* that her movement has beauty and form.

"There's another ritual to learn, too—group hierarchy. Outsiders might think it's best to be in the first group. But a dance student soon learns that the second group is best because she can watch the first group perform the combination and learn from their mistakes. But she has to make sure she gets the center spot in the second group where the teacher will notice her and nobody will block her view of the mirror. . . ."

"The thin mirror, right?" George asked.

"The thin mirror." She grinned. "You're catching on."

"All this sounds so complicated. I would have thought the hardest part was the dancing."

"Dancing's the easy part. It's just a matter of energy, pain, and discipline. Stretching the hamstrings, for example. It hurts like hell. I used to stretch them on my bedroom barre and in the doorway. Once I tried to show off for Daddy. I went to the door of his study and put my foot above my head, placed the heel against the door frame, and straightened my knee until the entire length of my leg was flush against the frame, my forehead pressed against my knee. I don't think he realized I was there for a while, he was so engrossed in his newspaper. So I just stood there, holding that standing split, until he glanced up and noticed me. He didn't react at all."

George said, "That sounds like quite a feat, Emily."

"It's simply a matter of flexibility. You work through the pain. Each day you stretch a little more. It's like any athlete, just gradual day-by-day conditioning.

"Within a year I was the best in the class. All the other girls were more interested in boys and being cheerleaders. A couple of older women were just looking for exercise. And pretty soon I'd learned everything Miss Charlotte could teach me. I was starting to think about where I could go to learn more. *Dance Magazine* gave me the idea of going to New York. All the wonderful things in dance were happening in New York.

"I guess that sounds crazy, doesn't it? I mean, a ten-year-old kid wanting to go to New York by herself. But that was typical of me. I didn't have any fear then. But now these last three years, the last few weeks. . . . Well, that's why I called you. It was because of fear, my total lack of courage. Uh, what time is it? Do we have five more minutes?"

"Of course."

"It took me two years of work and planning. I used the same tactics as before, but on a larger scale. I made up a brief. It wasn't a letter; it was a legal presentation. I went to the library and studied more biographies of famous dancers and outlined the details of their early training. Then I studied an anatomy book to learn that the bones and muscles are pretty well formed by the early teens. It was proof that my professional dance training couldn't be postponed until after high school.

"Fourteen pages, that brief was. I waited for a day when my father seemed to have had a good day at the office, and requested an appointment. That tickled him. Me, his daughter, asking for an appointment like any business associate. But I had him figured absolutely right. When I entered his study for the appointment he made a big show of removing and cleaning his glasses, folding the newspaper, and fussing with the pencils on his desk. You see, those were the delaying tactics he used to keep the upper hand over the business people who came to see him. But I just waited patiently for him to finish his routine.

"Then I made my presentation, explained everything, and answered every question. And it worked. He made a deal with my aunt and uncle in New York and arranged for me to live with them. He'd send some money for my tuition, and I'd pay my room and board. It was fantastic. There I was, still a tiny little girl, on my way to New York, alone. Just for the summer, but I didn't care. I knew I was going to be a real dancer.

"Oh what a celebration that night! It was warm. We opened all the windows and turned on every light in the house. I put a

44

Rachmaninoff concerto on the record player, turned it up loud, and sat at the piano pantomiming that I was playing. People on the sidewalk knew that something special was happening at the Frankel house that night. Even my sisters were happy. But then, the night before I left for New York, my father said the most terrible thing to me." Emily fell silent, remembering.

"My dear," her father had said to her, "I know you and our family better than you do. And you'll come to understand this better when you grow up.

"Our family has always had the potential for greatness, but none of us have the willpower to fulfill our ambitions. We always settle for something less."

She glanced up at George. "His voice was so cool and logical, like a professor. He told me, 'You may seem successful in your dance classes at Laurelton, but it's only because your classmates are inferior.'

"But Daddy," she had said, "Miss Charlotte says I'm really good."

"'I don't want to see you break your heart. You've just bluffed her with your words and energy. New York is no different from our town. You'll achieve something, I'm sure, but not real greatness.'"

She frowned, continued, "George, I can still hear what he said next. It's engraved on my mind. 'Emily, you and your sisters are the stepchildren of genius.'

"Some send-off," Emily recalled bitterly. "I lay there in bed that night. Daddy's favorite poem, 'Invictus,' kept going through my head. That's the agnostic's credo, you know, that poem. Daddy would never let us join a church; he didn't believe in God. But I did, secretly. That night before leaving for New York, I prayed to the only God I knew about. I had this picture of some great switchboard operator in the sky, plugging and unplugging prayers like they were telephone calls. I got on my knees, folded my hands, and said:

'God, I know you're awfully busy, so I'll only call you this once. I won't bother you with stuff like tests in school and things. I'll just ask you to help me be a dancer. And make me an unconquerable soul, God, please.'

"And that night, George, I made a pact. I promised God that I would dance until I died. Until I died. It was a real vow,

George, a commitment like a nun makes. And it all happened the way I prayed it would. I *did* go to New York and study dancing. I *did* become a dancer, a good one. And for a while, I *was* unconquerable, never getting discouraged, just growing and learning and moving ahead in my dancing. I formed a company. We toured the world.

"And then, George, everything began coming apart." She was very quiet, but she wanted to shout. It wasn't my fault. I tried. I tried. I worked harder than anybody.

George glanced obviously at his watch, but she missed the hint. "I came home from Europe. I broke up the company. John was making a movie out West and I went with him. Those were the worst months of my life. We never talked about my failure and my suspicions. I just closed myself in, never went out of the hotel room, kept the drapes drawn all day. I found his address book; there were a couple names in it, girls' names. In my frame of mind, I decided they'd been his girl friends when I was out of town. So I threw my wedding ring out the window. My name was in the book, too. Under 'Nearest Relative' he had written, 'Emily Frankel, Wife.' And I crossed out my own name and wrote 'DEAD.'"

"Emily," he interrupted, "I hate to break in, but it's time. We can finish this tomorrow."

"Oh, George, help me, please. . . ."

George didn't smile. He just opened the door. "You remember how your Daddy's poem ends, Emily? It's one of my favorites too, you know. 'It matters not how strait the gate, / How charged with punishments the scroll, / I am the master of my fate: / I am the captain of my soul.'"

"Master of my fate, / Captain . . ." she mused on the taxi ride home. I finally broke the dam and talked about what was really important, didn't I? Tomorrow, I'll tell him about going to New York the first time, when I was—what, eleven? No, twelve. A little captain, that's what I was. . . .

4.

From Harrisburg to Manhattan

What do you do when you're a tiny twelve-year-old girl, on the first train trip alone of your life, and you haven't enough money in your pocket to tip the porter?

He was so solicitous. "How about a pillow for that pretty red head, Little Lady? Long trip to New York."

She was trying so hard to *look* grown-up. She huddled against the window, pretending an interest in the dull scenery, hoping he would leave her alone. Later she saw him coming toward her from the end of the car. Quickly she dropped her chin to her chest, pretending sleep. He shook her shoulder. "Dining car's open. Better get you something. Little Ladies like you got big appetites."

She had already consumed the sandwich her mother had packed, and there wasn't enough money for a dining car meal. "I'm a dancer. I'm not supposed to eat much. Not good for my figure."

At Penn Station, despite her weak protests, the porter insisted on carrying her bags. She walked alongside him, eyes on the ground, afraid to simply admit that she didn't have enough money for an appropriate tip. The fear itself was frightening to a little girl who had whipped her older sister in fistfights, who had challenged the imposing authority of her father and won. He's a porter, she said to herself, and they live on tips.

"I'm not supposed to go all the way out here with you," he chattered as they moved through the terminal. "But I guess someday you'll be a big ballet star, get your picture in the newspapers. I can tell my friends I know you."

She asked him to leave her bags by the bank of telephones where she would call her aunt and uncle. She didn't meet his eyes, mumbled "Thank you."

"Now you be a good dancer, Little Lady. She saw the kindness in his eyes, impulsively reached up and hugged him, kissed his cheek. "Thank you, thank you again," she whispered.

Her relatives' small house in Queens suffered in comparison to the spacious Frankel home in Harrisburg. And worst of all was the lack of privacy. At home, she had her own room. But Uncle Mort and Aunt Hannah had provided only a curtained-off portion of the hallway between kitchen and back porch. There was barely enough room for a cot and chest of drawers.

It seemed there was no solution to that problem, at least not yet. She decided simply to adapt. Anyway, she wouldn't be spending much time there. Her energies were reserved for the Metropolitan Ballet School.

And what an intimidating place the school was. Where she had competed with tens of students at Laurelton, here there were hundreds, come from all over the country for the special summer dance curriculum. Emily was not a joiner, and no one invited her to join the cliques which were forming. Few, in fact, even noticed the lonely little girl who came and went so quietly.

Many students came from wealthy families. Their parents would appear at noon to whisk them off to lunch, while Emily was left behind with only a sandwich she had brought. In a corner of the studio, trying to eat slowly, she would try to stretch the sandwich into a fifteen-minute meal. Many days, there wasn't even a sandwich.

What does a hungry twelve-year-old do? Emily walked,

48

finally discovering an Automat several blocks away. Two nickles bought her an iced tea and all the sugar and lemon she could load on her saucer. Dessert was a return to the counter for refills of sugar and lemon.

What happens to a little girl, alone and hungry in such a big city? Emily's answer set a pattern that would sustain her the rest of her life. The answer was work. By not going to lunch, she could work extra time at the barre and she was able to study the real dancers who had their classes after the summer students were finished.

A haughty, superior group, these privileged few were professionals, members of companies. Never had Emily seen such dancing. Adagios were smoother, more controlled; allegros faster, lighter, swifter; arabesques higher; pirouettes more balanced— three, four, five, and six turns in perfect sequence. These people were the pictures in Emily's bedroom shrine back home come to life.

Just standing, waiting at the barre, they looked different from everyone else. Where most of Emily's fellow students came to class dressed as if to perform, these people were a scraggly lot. Sweaty leotards, often torn, usually patched. Baggy wool leg-warmers. Shapeless gray sweaters. Girls' hair pinned up, stringy ends sticking out. Nondescript ballet slippers, scuffed and scraped, occasionally mismatched even in color.

What was it that set them apart? It was more than their ragged dress. Nor was it simply their easy camaraderie and snobbish élan. It was a quality of steel core centered in flesh and bone, the original iron which has survived heat and pressure. Steel they were, to their very toes.

Their toes were expressive and articulate. They could achieve so many turns on their toes, or in *relevé*. Emily decided she could have feet like that, too—toes as expressive as fingers, as supple and articulate as a deaf mute's hands. She set aside time each day for special exercises, ten minutes a foot. She stretched her arches, trying to make the smooth, flat top of her foot into a rounded hill. She commanded her toes to respond as fingers: little toe down, little toe up; big toe sideways, big toe back. If I stretch my feet more than the professionals, she reasoned, my feet will become even more expressive. I'll catch up to them. If they are steel at eighteen, I can be steel at twelve.

Of course, there was pain. The body hurts when forced to

49

go beyond what nature intended. A full split had hurt when she first tried it, but she kept working until she could go all the way to the floor without even slightly bouncing down. An ache in the Achilles tendon at the back of the right heel developed. But she persevered. She wanted to be steel, and she welcomed the fire.

Boris Novikoff, equal parts Russian dance master and dictator, noticed Emily's constant practice. His attention meant that she was in for more than her share of canings. Not that Novikoff ever actually struck students, but he had grown up in the harsh discipline of the Russian ballet schools in the days when it was considered quite appropriate to beat erring students.

He reluctantly understood that in America, children were spoiled and spared. Still, the shiny black knotted cane remained his personal symbol of authority, wielded with the finesse of a fencing master, stopping a controlled hairsbreadth from actual contact. He stabbed at offending hips, stopping the lunge just short of the target. Or the cane would flash down, cracking the barre an inch from a graceless wrist.

To a twelve-year-old, it was a terrifying warning. From across the large studio, thronged with fifty gyrating students, Novikoff would suddenly materialize at her side, slashing his cane and shouting, "The hip! The hip, little girl. You no vant to be good? You dance like skating on ice!" She did not yet understand that Novikoff's shouts indicated his interest in her. Emily worked with one eye on the mirrors and other dancers, the other on the teacher's whereabouts.

She learned to keep a wary eye on her surroundings on the subway as well. Like her first trip to Queens from the school. It was rush hour, no seats were available, and she was too small to reach the grab handles. Emily managed to squirm through the crowds to an aisle pole, but the massed bodies obscured her view of the station names. To make matters worse, someone's hand was sliding toward her buttocks; she wasn't sure whose hand, in the crush. She had to escape, had to get off the train and away. But where? How?

Remembering her lesson with the porter on the train, she told herself, use common sense, Emily. Do what seems most practical. She pushed through the car, found the conductor and stayed with him until the next stop.

Most twelve-year-old girls could go to their parents for

consolation, for comfort, for advice. But for Emily, there was no one, not even Aunt Hannah and Uncle Mort.

In bed at night, she could hear them discussing her. "You can see her father in her," Uncle Mort would comment. "He's always been a dreamer. Why, he'll bore you to death talking about that damn book he was going to write and never got around to it. Now Emily's just like all the Frankels—dreamers, not doers. She'll probably wind up a nervous housewife just like her mother."

Oh, no I won't, Emily vowed to the stars. Zephyr will never wind up "just a housewife." Emily's answer to the problem was again more work. If I spend more time at school and less time in Queens, I won't have to listen to them. But to take more classes, she needed more money. And what does a twelve-year-old girl, alone in New York, do to earn money?

She summoned the courage to ask the school's forbidding secretary about available jobs. There was a scholarship opening. In return for reduced tuition, Emily performed janitorial duties at the school, cleaning the toilets and dressing rooms after evening classes. She swept out the studios, turned off the lights, and locked the door when she left.

To speed the tedium of her nightly labors, she invented a small choreography, a short *pas de deux* with her broom, to the tune she hummed. And having a key to the school meant she could come in during hours when it was normally closed—early morning, weekends, late at night—and practice alone with the barre, mirrors, and record player.

Even with the scholarship, Emily couldn't afford all the extra classes she wanted to take. She looked for a part-time job, walked long distances on hard city sidewalks to answer want ads. The pain in her Achilles tendon intensified, shot up her calf with a lightning jab. Novikoff noticed she was limping. He insisted she see a doctor who specialized in dancer's injuries.

After examining her feet, the doctor, his assistant, and his nurse discussed her condition as if she wasn't even in the room.

"Chronic inflammation of the Achilles tendon," she heard. "Flat feet, wrong bone structure for a dancer. Never make it with those feet. Just to walk normally, she'll need a cast, an ankle brace or tight bandage, crutches for a while. Above all, no dancing. Not until the inflammation is cured."

Novikoff was sorry, but the doctor's recommendation must be followed. There was no point in a student compounding an injury, now was there? Better to rest. No dancing. Scholarship cancelled. Return home.

It would have been a crushing defeat, except for two treasures: she had learned the concept of steel and fire; and she had the letter Novikoff had written to her parents. Emily opened it carefully, planning to reseal it before showing it at home.

Dear Mr. and Mrs. Frankel:
Miss Emily is very, very good student. She improves every day. If heel improves, she should have every day classes. She has great musicality. Is very lyrical, makes ballet as we were taught in Russia. In my opinion, she is born ballerina.

Sincere,
Boris Novikoff

For a year she remained in Harrisburg, never losing sight of her goal of returning to New York and dance school. While her mother and father pressured her to be a "normal" teenager and to finish junior high school, Emily returned to her cashier's job at Feller's Men's Wear and tried to heal the tendonitis.

For her graduation present from junior high, her father agreed to another summer in New York.

Then she was back for her "Second Chance" summer. Instead of staying with relatives, she rented a room in a boarding house for young women. Replacing the Metropolitan Ballet School and Novikoff were the school for American Ballet and George Balanchine, who was building the New York City Ballet Company.

With the help of one of the teachers, there was again a work scholarship of janitorial duties. This time, she got an additional job as a messenger girl for J.C. Penney, marching sturdily along the city sidewalks, munching oatmeal cookies. She loved oatmeal cookies, which was fortunate because they were all she could afford after paying for the expanded dance class schedule and her room.

52

The job didn't help her feet. The tendonitis had not healed, and favoring the sore foot caused tendonitis in her left heel.

Still, she learned to work with the pain, developing her own technique. Point work was excruciating, but she could *relevé*, and go to three-quarter point by taking the weight on the outsides of her feet. She thought she was doing reasonably well until the week before the summer session was to end. Her teacher, Oboukhoff, one of the great Pavlova's partners, asked her to meet him in the office after class. She was not being asked to join the Balanchine company, as she had fantasized, but once again was being sent home.

It was all happening again. But instead of a letter, she had her teacher's uplifting words:

"Emily, I am sorry, but regular season students return to school soon, take scholarship jobs. And too much pain in your feet to continue work now. You try too much, perhaps injure permanent." She tried to explain, to argue, to plead. He waved a hand.

"No, little Emily. Too soon, too soon. You very strong. Good possibility for ballerina. But too much work, too much walk, hurt ankle. Go home now. Rest. Then come back. Come back here. I will work with you then."

Dear Sara,

Can I please come stay with you at college? Daddy and Mama want me to come home. But you know what that means—they want me to conform, be like the other kids, date and go to football games, wear "teenage" clothes, etc. And you know me. I tried to be what they wanted me to be the last time I was at home, and it didn't work. I promise I won't be any bother to you at school. I proved I can get and keep a job this summer in New York. So if you'll let me stay with you for a little while, I'll move out and get my own place as soon as I find a way to support myself.

Love,
Emily

She joined Sara at Antioch College in Ohio. Within a week she had found a job aiding the college librarian in collating and book mending. Within two weeks she was taking dance class with the college students. In a month, too young to be enrolled as a regular student, she began auditing standard curriculum courses.

A friend recommended the University of Chicago which had an experimental program of college courses for young people who possessed college-level intelligence but were not of college age.

Emily enrolled at the university, took the entrance exams, was placed at the fourth-year college level, and advised to major in physics or mathematics.

Despite her academic achievement, Zephyr was not forgotten. Emily studied dance at the university, and at the city's largest ballet school. Balanchine's company was on a national tour, and Emily bought a ticket. Sitting in the balcony, she watched the magic performance of such dancers as Maria Tallchief, André Eglevsky, Melissa Hayden, and Frank Moncion. She thought, those dancers don't have college degrees. What am I wasting my time for? I belong back in New York, studying to dance like them.

On the back of a picture postcard showing the university's gothic buildings, one of several she bought, she wrote:

> Dear Mom and Dad:
> Spring term is over and I got good grades again, thank goodness. All A's. I'm staying in Chicago for Summer Session. My love to everybody.
>
> Emily

Just before leaving for the train station and New York, she left a note in her best friend's mailbox. "I'm off to New York. I know my parents would never permit it, so please do me a favor. I've written and addressed a bunch of postcards which I'm leaving with you. If you'd mail one a month, I'd appreciate it. That way they'll think I'm still in Chicago. Thanks a lot. I'll write you from New York as soon as I get a permanent address. Thanks again, Em."

In her pocket were nine dollars and the name of a girl working in a pottery shop. Yes, the girl said, there was a part-time job

54

at the shop. Yes, Emily could share her apartment. To Emily's acute discomfort, her share of the apartment turned out to be the living-room couch, well within earshot of the bedroom where the girl cavorted with a succession of men.

Not yet fifteen, truly on her own in New York, no longer a little girl, and still the same old problems: privacy; money for shelter and food and, most of all, dance lessons.

Apartments for rent could be found in the classified ads. One day she climbed the stairs of a five-floor walk-up on West Fifteenth Street. The landlady showed Emily into a filthy, six-room cold-water railroad flat. Emily's nostrils informed her that many rodents had found their final resting place there.

"You're lucky, dearie," said the landlady. "Just put it on the market. You're the first one to see it."

One step ahead of the wrecking ball, Emily thought.

"Of course, you have to provide your own heat and hot water," the lady hastened to add, "But at thirty-six dollars a month, the price is right. You can't beat it."

Emily quickly learned the New York tenement technique of midnight scavenging—furnishing one's apartment with curbside castoffs. She found an upholstered chair atop a pile of garbage on a Greenwich Village street. It's a beautiful chair, she thought. I could clean the dirt off easily. And it doesn't matter that one arm is broken off. If I can't fix it, I'll just set that side against the wall.

Behind a grocery store, she discovered a treasure trove of orange crates. She could make her own dining-room table and chairs. She could turn them into an end-table and desk. She located a used bed at the Salvation Army and disinfected it. She painted every-thing orange.

The walls needed a mural. That, she already knew how to do. In Harrisburg, she had painted a 5 by 10 foot picture on the wall of her school cafeteria. With even more wall space at her disposal, she painted a panorama of gold and orange and green, a brilliant city within her home. The tenement had become her "Orange Palace."

Emily even discovered a way to live rent-free. She kept two front rooms for herself and fixed up the other four to rent out as studios. On hands and knees, she scrubbed years' worth of machine oil and sawdust off the floor and walls using No. 1 steel wool. With a razor blade, she scraped city grime from the windows. Next she attacked the cooking grease buildup on the ancient stove. Calling on her dance-school janitorial experience, she cleaned the toilet, then went out and found an old sink in a junkyard and installed the plumbing herself.

And when her tenants objected that they were paying the same rent for a studio as she was for a two-room apartment, she went downtown to City Hall and got herself licensed as probably the youngest landlady ever in the city of New York.

At progressive Antioch, and later in Chicago, Emily had been exposed briefly to modern dancing. It was different and exciting—free, flowing, light. Expression of mood and interpretation of a story were encouraged. It was time to branch out. A newspaper had led her to the New Dance Group where—for ninety-eight cents a lesson, provided she signed up for three packages of ten lessons each—she studied Hindu, folk, and Spanish dancing, and the techniques of Martha Graham, Hanya Holm, and Charles Weidman.

The New Dance Group had no scholarship program, and to pay for all this, she needed something besides her pottery shop paycheck.

Dance Magazine needed a Promotions Director. She said she was twenty-one, majoring in journalism and public relations in college. Knowing that they would never hire a girl who might leave the staff for the stage, she didn't admit to being a dancer; instead, she talked about her deep and abiding interest in public relations. She got the job.

But still she needed money. Hair braided like a Russian princess and piled in a high crown secured by a black velvet band, bra padded, high heels clicking, she went for yet another job interview. This time she said she was a college graduate with a master's degree in social work. She didn't worry that the city required teacher certification, figuring that she'd work until someone told her to stop.

She was given supervision of a playground in the heart of the ghetto. Many of the hard-core delinquents—tough black and Hispanic youngsters—were her own age or older and many were physically stronger. The first day with her class, she said, "Look, you have managed to get your previous teachers fired. So I'm telling you right now, you're not going to get rid of me because I'm starving and I need this job. We're all in the same fix, so let's cooperate." The settlement-house youngsters could identify with this gutsy little lady who brought a bag of oatmeal cookies and told them, "This is my meal for the day. No lunch, dinner, or breakfast, but the whole day."

Emily would learn a dance step in class one evening and teach it to her students the next morning. Entering the area by bus, she would be met by a welcoming committee: "Emily's here. The Oatmeal Cookie Dancer." Mornings were spent in the Bronx; early afternoon hours at *Dance Magazine*, where she could often be found in the stockroom with her aching feet propped up; late afternoons at the New Dance Group; and finally evening classes at the School for American Ballet; followed by the janitorial wrap-up.

It became more and more difficult to mask the pain in her heels. Her ballet teacher, Oboukhoff, advised her, "I'm sorry, but you waste your time, and ours, in formal ballet training. In my opinion you will never have perfect point technique for ballerina. Not that you are meant for corps de ballet. You phrase music too special. Your arms, good arms, for a prima ballerina, not for corps. But your feet, *they* are corps de ballet."

Giving up ballet meant giving up her dream of tutus and satin toe shoes. On the other hand, her work with the New Dance Group had convinced her that she might develop her own language of movement, and some day convey her attitudes and opinions of the times in which she was living. Perhaps it would be a good thing to be free of the constraints of classical ballet and the necessity for carbon-copy execution of movement rituals based on formal court manners of the 1600s.

There was, in addition, a practical reason. In modern dance, which does not rely on point technique, she might be able to bypass her chronic heel problems.

Charles Weidman was one of the major modern dancers in the United States. She visited his New York school, signed up for classes, and obtained the by-now inevitable work scholarship.

His classes were the most stimulating she had ever taken. There was floor work as well as jumping. Weidman emphasized rhythm, played drums as he taught. He picked the class music to fit the exercise—jazz, Latin, classical, whatever was appropriate. At Weidman's the little girl who loved to dress up and play-act found a wonderful outlet for expression. For the first time, she experienced movement flowing from dramatic interpretation and imagery, not ritual. And she was encouraged to use her imagination and individuality.

Soon she discovered she could do the same steps everyone else was doing, and make the steps look different. Instead of strict dancing, four equal beats to the measure, for example, she'd hold the last count—like holding one's breath—then come in fast on the first count of the next measure.

Her excitement was apparent to everyone in the school. At last she had found a dance home, temporary maybe, but a place where she could stay a while and grow. Her joy and energy were contagious, and Emily was making friends.

She became close to the wardrobe mistress. Staying late for her scholarship work, Emily began helping out in the costume room. The two spent hours trying on costumes, giggling through impromptu *pas de deux* among the dusty props and trunks.

A boy in the company stayed late to help with the cleaning chores, filling Emily in on company gossip: who was living with whom; Maida, the company's lead girl, who was jealous of everybody and did her best to make the other dancers look bad.

Though it was suspected the assistant stage manager stole money from the girls' purses, Emily rather liked him. He let her help move sets and props, run a traveling spot from the catwalk, check sound levels in various parts of the theater during rehearsals.

The company's pianist lived near Emily. Often the two walked home together, the woman telling Emily she was more musical than the other dancers.

A girl who was a veteran member of the company offered advice on stretching the feet and how to achieve a more perfectly arched foot.

The company's male lead dancer showered praise on her, saying she was already a better dancer than Maida.

One particular evening, one of the girls became sick during rehearsal and Emily was asked to fill in. Just like that, with no fanfare, Emily was a member of the company. A tour had been booked, the itinerary posted, and Emily's name was on the traveling list.

As an official member of the company, almost a professional, Emily redoubled her efforts. On breaks, when the rest of the company would head for a cup of coffee or cigarette in the hall, Emily stayed in the studio, practicing. She always reported to rehearsal early.

"If everybody came in early like Emily," Weidman told the company, "we could start rehearsals on time."

Emily suggested, "Why don't we have a warm-up class every day like they do in ballet companies? That way, nobody will be late, and we'll all be really warmed up for rehearsal. I'll be glad to get it organized, get people to sign up."

Weidman was delighted with her idea; the company members considerably less so. They were all affected by this youngest member of their company. Many of them had been on the payroll for years. They were irritated by her brashness. Then Emily was assigned her first solo role. It was an unprecedented achievement for a newcomer, a tribute to her talent and hard work. The company members were alternately annoyed, impressed, resentful, amused, and jealous.

Many dark looks were sent her way, but Emily was too happy to notice.

Filling out the company employment form, the secretary asked, "Where's your home?"

Emily answered, "I'm a New Yorker!"

5.
With The Weidman Dance Company

Full of confidence, eager to begin, Emily arrived early. Thirty minutes before rehearsal, she warmed up alone on the stage of Weidman's studio theater. The rest of the company was resisting Emily's idea of a warm-up class before rehearsals.

Weidman entered from the back of the theater, carrying a stack of records. Walking down the aisle toward the stage, he did not meet Emily's eyes. The rest of the company followed him, taking seats in the front two rows. None of the usual lighthearted company chatter; they, too, were silent. Emily waited patiently, watching the group.

At last Weidman spoke, concentrating on the records in his hands. "Emily, the company has come to me. They . . . gave me an ultimatum. They refuse to go on tour—unless I fire you."

"What?" But they were her friends, they respected her.

"They say you have made it impossible for them to work.

61

They say you are a know-it-all, that you don't know your place. That you have disrupted their work, that you don't take direction."

Emily couldn't think of anything to say.

The young man who had told her she was better than Maida, said, "She's sneaky, Charles. She doesn't do the combinations right. She executes the movements a little different from everybody else, changes the phrasing, adds her own details, so the audience will only watch her instead of the whole company."

But what I do adds to the performance, she thought, I'm not trying to look different, I'm trying to make the whole company look better.

The girl who had offered advice on toe-pointing exercises stood up. "Charles, she's got such terrible technique. Her feet don't point. Her hands are stiff, and she doesn't try to improve, either."

Maida was next. "She's wearing my costume. Who gave her permission?"

"But you told the wardrobe mistress you didn't want it for rehearsals," Emily tried to explain. "I just thought it would help me handle the long skirt when we got into full costume . . ."

"You're always snooping around in the costume room," Maida broke in, "taking the best for yourself."

"That's right," added the wardrobe mistress. "Emily just takes what she wants, without even asking. And she leaves the costume room in a mess. Takes me an hour to straighten up after she's been poking around."

"She has no musicality at all," said the pianist. "And she's always wasting my time, clinging to me like a leech, gossiping about other people in the company."

The assistant director spoke up. "She should worry about what people say about her. Have you noticed how she always sits in the corner when the rest of us take a coffee break? Maybe that's why the money's been disappearing from the purses."

Weidman stood and hurled the records at the wall. Black shards of plastic scattered over the seats.

On it went, a Salem witch trial in New York. Emily stood without moving, tears of anger and fear and incomprehension streaming down her cheeks. Finally, Weidman spoke. "All right, that's enough. Emily, you're excused from rehearsal today."

She went home and tried to figure out what had gone

wrong. Staring around her little apartment, she saw ugly orange crates and cast-off furniture nobody else had wanted. She knew that the grimy windows overlooked an alley filled with garbage dumped from people's windows. She sat and wondered what to do.

Late that night her telephone rang. It was Weidman. "Emily, rehearsal is at three o'clock tomorrow. Be here."

"But, Charles, I thought—"

"Never mind. *I* want you here. It's too late to replace you. You'll just have to rethink your attitude and learn to get along with the company. Three o'clock!"

She pondered what had happened. Of course it made sense. Realistically, Weidman could not fire her—too much rehearsal time and money were at stake. The other dancers knew that to find a replacement for her now would mean delaying or canceling the tour, only two weeks away. Nor was there any question of her refusing. She was a member of a company, and her choreographer had told her to be there.

But how should she act? She needed a public face with which to face her attackers. Weidman was right in a way; she needed to change her attitude, find a way to fit herself into the company. Her fear and anger prompted the solution: She would be gracious and charming and make small talk, keeping her opinions, ambition, and intelligence forever hidden behind a wall of obedient cooperation. She would be polite as a Southern belle, say what they expected to hear.

Accused of showing up the other dancers, she was careful to arrive exactly at three, no earlier. She warmed up at home before leaving for the studio. Checking the bulletin board, she saw that she had been removed from three of her four solo roles. But Weidman had left her her favorite, the slave girl in "House Divided," his story about Lincoln's freeing of the slaves.

The company did not welcome her with open arms. When she smiled tentatively at Carl, the male lead, he turned his head away. She spoke to the pianist, who was sipping coffee. The woman pretended not to hear. But at least no one attacked her. The company had achieved its purpose. She had been scolded publicly, and the bit parts, for which all young dancers compete, had been taken away from her.

Clearly, she could no longer risk volunteering for extra work that could incur the others' jealousy. Instead, she would do only what was required. Her reward was the silent treatment. No one acknowledged her existence. No one spoke to her, unless it was terse, necessary, onstage choreography direction.

When the tour began, she was prepared. There were plenty of strong young men in the company, but when they assembled at Grand Central Station, there was no one to help her with her luggage. On board the train, no one sat with her. They gathered around each other's seats in tight, chattering little groups. When Emily made a tentative effort to join them, they lapsed into stony silence until she returned to her seat—then burst into laughter and whispers.

One, however, did not participate in the ostracism— Frank Udell, the company's road manager. He dropped into the seat beside Emily. "Guess we outcasts have to stick together, right?"

Be careful she thought. Don't trust anybody. "What do you mean?"

"Road managers are never exactly popular. I'm not a member of the company, just hired to run the tour. I do all the administrative dirty work. Arrange for hotels, group meals, pay salaries, make everybody keep to the schedule. That sort of stuff."

"So what do you do during our rehearsals?"

"Read, mostly—technical stuff. I want to be a stage manager on Broadway one of these days, so I study on the train."

"What are you studying now?"

"Lighting systems. There's a lot of new equipment out now. Some new automated systems are almost miraculous in what they can do. I want to read up on them. All the big theaters will be installing them soon. I want to be ready."

It was just the kind of thing that fascinated Emily: new ways of accomplishing old tasks. She asked to borrow one of Udell's books and spent much of the trip reading. In the final hours before their arrival, she captured his attention with a steady stream of questions.

"I'm afraid you didn't get much studying done," she said as they got off the train.

64

"Hey, listen, it's okay. You ask good questions, and you force me to know the subject better so I can teach you. This is the best trip I've had in a long time."

"I'm glad you don't mind," Emily answered. "You make being an outcast fun."

At the hotel the company lined up at the registration desk for room assignments. Emily discovered that her name was listed alone; nobody wanted to room with her. Since dancers on the road pay their own expenses, sharing a room is the standard way of saving money. In the line there was much good-natured horseplay, but Emily could not take part. Instead she waited patiently at the end, wondering what to do.

Finally, when Emily stood alone before the desk clerk, she asked, "Sir, do you have any room for servants? Or rooms without baths?"

He was insulted. This was the finest hotel in Lafayette, Indiana, favored because of its proximity to the Purdue campus. He was sorry, but there were no such rooms.

"Is there another hotel nearby that might cost less?"

She was directed to a shabby little establishment five blocks away, bearing a neon sign advertising "Transients—$4 a night." It was a small hotel with a dingy lobby and a narrow staircase up from the street. And she had to carry her own luggage. Emily ignored the lascivious stares from sitters in the lobby, endured the desk clerk's rude remarks, and settled for a room without bath for $2.50 a night.

The Weidman company was booked for a week at Purdue. During the days the dancers taught classes and rehearsed; in the evenings they performed. Afterward, they partied at campus hang-outs. Emily, of course, was never invited. Instead, she returned to her room. With pencil and notebook she gave each performance a complete going-over, movement by movement, grading herself on the difficult technical feats, envisioning how she had done a certain phrase dramatically, musically, and what she could do to improve it for the next performance.

Emily was teaching herself to be her own mirror, seeing herself as if from an orchestra seat.

Let the others paint the town red, she thought. This is my fun. But despite Emily's mental activity, there were still lonely hours

65

to fill. She assisted the stage crew, volunteering to help anybody and everybody. Most of all, she helped Udell.

Purdue was equipped with an Izenour board, one of the most complicated and technically advanced lighting systems in the country. Scrambling through the overhead pipes, climbing ladders, plugging and unplugging, Emily quickly learned about dimmers, presets, power lines, and how to wire a three-strand plug. She discovered gels, their color numbers, how to cut them and frame them. She learned the different kinds of lighting fixtures—Lekos, Fresnells, Ellipsoidals, arc spots—how to focus them, their differing functions. It was an exciting moment when she realized that instead of rejecting her ideas, Udell listened and discussed them with her.

At the end of the week, the company assembled in the railroad station. Udell distributed the week's reviews. Like a teacher's report card, the critics' reviews were a standard against which dancers could measure their own effectiveness. Emily stood alone, excluded as usual. The other dancers read, then silently glared at her.

Of all the dancers in the company, only Emily was mentioned by name: "The role of the slave girl in 'House Divided,' danced by Emily Frankel, was easily the *tour de force* moment of the entire evening. A tiny girl, she stands head and shoulders above the other dancers in her company. Her mastery of technique, subtleties of movement, expression, and ability to produce extremes of emotion in her audience, remind one of the greats of the past." The review, of course, did little to enhance Emily's popularity with her fellow dancers. And there was more of the same throughout the tour.

By the time they returned to New York, her feelings about Weidman's company were confused. She took the problem to Weidman.

"Charles, what should I do? I want to stay with the company. And I think I've earned better roles."

He thought a moment. "You're the best dramatic dancer right now, in the company. You've worked hard, and I know what you've had to put up with from the others. And it's only going to get worse, too. Now you're learning firsthand about professional jealousy.

"You have earned better roles. But Emily, I'm afraid I can't give them to you. The others will threaten to quit again. You

66

see, you have your dream, and mine is this company. I've worked a long time to put it together, and I'd lose it if I gave you any more of the featured roles."

With further progress barred, Emily knew she must leave Weidman. She was well-grounded in formal ballet, and she now had Weidman's technique. She had already begun her study of other forms—folk, ballroom, jazz, Hindu—and she knew it was time to experience first-hand the other "schools" of modern dance, Martha Graham's technique, for example.

"You'll understand, won't you, Charles, why I have to resign my scholarship here, and sign up as a regular student with Martha?"

"Of course. Neither I nor anyone else has the right to hold you back in your development as a dancer. I believe you have the potential to go beyond all of us.

"I would only hope that you stay with the company. Of course you'll be paid. Maybe that money will help enough so you won't have to take all those jobs, or work as a janitor any more."

A full-fledged professional dancer, earning a salary for her work—and free to expand and develop herself! Once again, her apartment was an Orange Palace for a queen, a Zephyr.

Now's the time, Queen Emily said to herself. I don't have to be a janitor ever again. I've got a salary, and I can afford to take a chance. Why not get my own studio? A floor-through loft, maybe. I'll start looking tomorrow. It'll have to be at least 2,000 square feet. I'll put in mirrors, maybe rent it to companies, teach children, and choreograph, maybe . . . maybe. . . .

6.
The Dance
Drama Duo

"Who was *that*?"

The blond girl followed Emily's glance. "You mean you don't know who he is?"

Emily shook her head, still watching the disappearing back of the handsome, muscular man who had smiled at her as he passed.

"That's Mark Ryder. He's Martha's regular partner. The top male dancer in the company."

"I've heard of him, but I've never seen him before. He's nice looking."

"Sure he is. Every girl who takes class here thinks he's nice looking. Problem is, he knows it. They say he can have any girl in the company he wants."

"That's a lot of girls. There must be twelve, fourteen girls."

"And Martha doesn't like company members socializing

with each other. If you want to get along with Martha, you'd better leave Mark alone."

Emily saw it differently. Mark Ryder had a reputation as one of the best male modern dancers in New York. If she could make friends with him, he could teach her a lot about lifts and partnering. What a thrill it would be to perform a duet with him.

From Weidman, Emily was learning lyrical modern movement, open and communicative, highlighting the human characteristics of the dancers. Graham based her technique on contraction and release—the torso's ability to go from concave to arched—floorwork, and a primitive style of sculptured movement. Weidman made theatrical statements about real-life situations. His forte was humor, while Graham's forte was Greek legends and Freudian ideas.

Layer upon layer, starting from her foundation of classical ballet, Emily began to develop what would become her own particular style. The major elements were her natural lyricism, her unusual energy and physical strength, giving her movement a dangerous grace, always feminine, yet with an underlying power. Working with the Graham style and technique, Emily was adding her own lyrical arms and torso to the movements. Martha Graham noticed. While still a member of Weidman's company, Emily was asked to join Martha's.

"Well, well. I see you're on the company list."

Mark Ryder was standing behind Emily, looking over her shoulder at her name on the bulletin board. Though she had noticed him watching her from time to time in class, it was the first time he'd spoken to her.

"I didn't even know you knew my name."

He laughed. "I have my ways."

Supercilious, she thought. But he's a good dancer.

"I suppose you know you're making dance history," he continued. "Nobody's ever been a member of the Weidman company

70

and the Graham company at the same time. The techniques are too different—almost opposite."

"How'd you know I'm a member of the Weidman company?"

"Oh, I keep up."

Sneaky, too, she decided. But definitely interesting.

"Well, from what I hear, Mark—"

"Ah-hah. You know my name, too."

"Well," she mimicked him, "I keep up, too."

He got her message, chuckled, invited her for a cup of coffee after class.

Ryder filled Emily in on the inside information about Martha Graham's company, chattered away for an hour about his ideas on dancing, then asked about her opinions and the latest news from Weidman's company.

"I don't think I have much of a future there, Mark. If Weidman gives me good roles, the rest of the company will threaten to quit. But all the Graham company ever seems to do is rehearse and rehearse. When are we going out on tour?"

"Didn't you hear? Martha's season got postponed."

"Oh no. That means we'll just go on rehearsing," she sighed. "I'm learning all these wonderful techniques, but I'm not getting to perform on a stage, for people. And I need to earn some money. I don't want to go on scrubbing toilets."

She propped her chin in her hand and stared hard at Mark. "But what can you do about it?" he asked, uncomfortable under her gaze. "What are you thinking?"

"I've had an idea for a while. Want to hear it?"

"Sure."

"You and I can join up and tour as a duo."

Now it was his turn to stare at Emily. Finally he stammered, "But that's impossible. The last team to do that was Weidman and Doris Humphrey, and that was thirty years ago. And they had the same technical background. You have the Weidman technique, and I have the Graham technique. We're incompatible."

"But that's the whole point, Mark. Think about it for a minute. A Graham dancer and a Weidman dancer working together will be a first. We're both good dancers, and using both techniques, we can make something extraordinary."

71

"Well. . . ."

"I know you've proved you're ready to go out on your own. Do you think *I'm* good enough? Be honest."

"Sure you are. Martha thinks you're very good."

"If I sit around and wait for Graham company politics to move me up, it'll be years before I get the chance to be anything more than just a Graham dancer. Think of your career, too. You've been Martha's lead dancer for five years, and you're only known as a Graham dancer. Well, here's your chance to become a Ryder dancer—to make your own individual statement—"

"It's an exciting idea," he interrupted. "Of all the people I've known in dance, you're the first one I ever met who likes my ideas of combining drama and dance. But there are an awful lot of problems. The logistics—transportation, moving sets and costumes, lodging and food expenses. Tech stuff like lighting and sound. And how do we get bookings in the first place? And make it economically feasible? I don't know anything about all that. Do you?"

"We can learn. Let's try and see if we can do it."

"What about rehearsal space?"

"We can use my loft. It's got good studio space. We don't have to tell anybody about it yet, just keep our jobs with Martha and Charles, and work in our spare time and at night. We try choreography; we try to get bookings; we figure out costs. After we try to solve some of the problems—say two months from now—then we make a yes-or-no decision. But at least let's try."

"You're quite a woman for a little girl, Emily—and I mean that in a loving way. Okay, we'll try."

The first item on the two-month schedule was their concept. Both wanted to make dancing comprehensible to a general audience, rather than a special art form appealing only to the dance-educated, select few. Dramatic ideas were important—story-telling with movement as opposed to abstract movement for movement's sake. They arrived at a title: The Dance Drama Duo.

Their first priority, they decided, was a tour. Just as a Broadway show needs to break in on the road, so they felt the need to have a series of trial performances, working out their ideas before an audience. The idea of putting together choreography, of spending money for sets and costumes, with just a single New York debut performance in mind, seemed wrong to them, though that was the way most modern groups started. But how to get colleges to book them, or even know that the Dance Drama Duo existed?

"We'll use direct mail," Emily announced to Mark one evening after rehearsal. "That's what Weidman does. Only we'll be more thorough, more organized, than they are at Weidman's. What we need first of all is a complete list of all the colleges and universities in the country.

"I'm always the last one to leave Weidman's studio. I can borrow their card file for a night and copy it at home." Mark thought he could provide the Graham list—the secretary was one of his former girl friends.

After eliminating duplications between the two lists, they came up with about 4,000 addresses of colleges, dance schools, and social organizations.

"How much do you think we should charge?" Mark asked.

"I figure we can do it for two hundred and fifty a night."

He was astonished. "Nobody charges that little! From what I hear, five hundred a night is the minimum."

"Exactly. So some of these organizations that couldn't afford a regular group, even a small company, will figure we're a bargain—and they'll book us. Until we're known, we've got to use every sales technique there is. I'm going to offer them a free master lesson with every concert, too. Nobody's ever done that that I know of."

"But how can we make it on two-fifty a night?"

"By cutting corners. We buy a used car big enough to get our sets and props in. We'll keep our sets to a minimum, and we design them so they're compact and fold up. There are only two of us, so we can keep our food expenses down. We'll stay in cheap hotels or sleep in the car if we have to. If we can get just thirty performances, we can net eight thousand dollars and split it down the middle when we get home."

Emily began writing to the organizations on her list. She understood the value of the "personal" approach; instead of printed letters, she typed each letter herself on a second-hand portable. Each letter took about two minutes.

73

"What do you send them besides the letter?" Mark asked.

"A printed brochure," she answered, "with pictures and rates."

"But that's expensive," he argued. "How do we pay for it?"

She grinned. "Friendship and smiles go a long way. You know Gus, the photographer? He needs some part-time secretarial work. I can do that for him in return for our pictures. And the man across the street is a printer. I gave his children some ballet lessons and never charged him, so he owes me a favor. He'll bill us for the brochures, but he'll let us pay him in installments out of the money we earn on the tour."

"All right, all right. I surrender. You've got everything worked out. I can't believe the way your mind works, your energy. I ought to marry you. What a perfect wife you'd be."

"Careful, Mark. I might take you up on your offer."

It took days upon days of typing to complete the letters and envelopes, and an additional week to fold, stuff, stamp and seal. And another week for their first responses to come back.

"Who's this Harriet Schaeffer?" Mark asked, sorting through the mail. "I've got three letters here addressed to her." He began to write "Not at this address" on the envelopes. "I'll leave these for the mailman to pick up in the morning."

"Wait. Harriet Schaeffer is me."

"You?"

"Yes. I didn't think it was right for Emily the dancer to be booking our tour. So I invented Harriet. She's our booking agent, but she doesn't get the usual twenty percent. Let me see those. They might be bookings."

The first letter she opened was from Purdue University. "What a coincidence, Mark. The first time I ever performed was at Purdue, with Weidman's company. And now our first booking will be at Purdue. The head of the department says she remembers me. Isn't that something? You never know how things will pay off in the future, do you?"

Mark, reading ahead, said, "She says she has to know what's on our program."

"But we don't have a program yet."

74

"What?" he teased. "You mean you haven't figured that out, too? I thought you had everything planned."

She ignored him. "Come on. Let's start planning our program. We'll get it out in the mail tomorrow. I don't want them giving the date to somebody else because we don't have a program."

"A whole program? In one night?"

"Sure. We'll suggest titles. The ones we like will be our program. We already know the kinds of things we want to do. All we have to do is put titles to them."

"I don't know. Seems kind of backwards to me." Mark shrugged. "But, okay, let's try it."

Hundreds of titles were suggested, most rejected. Of the fifty or so they liked, seven were picked—a solo for each of them and five duets. Each dance work would have a different style and story content. There was a contemporary piece; a waltz, light and balletic; one traditional and dramatic. Though no choreography yet existed, it was during that long night of talk that the Dance Drama Duo came to life. The discussion produced a clear concept of what Mark and Emily, together, wanted to "say" in dance.

Emily borrowed a blank contract from Weidman and adapted it to their needs. It, along with their program, was mailed to Purdue. In two weeks they received their first signed booking agreement.

Next came the labor of choreography. She had no training, no theories, only the instinctive understanding that total immersion in the music was the first step to building a dance work. They selected music they both liked, then worked for hours, listening to each phrase—eight times, ten, even fifteen—with each repetition developing and refining the movement from a basic pantomimic level to one of abstraction, which still retained the communicative element. The process was much like that of an artist shaping a piece of modeling clay into a rough form, then squeezing, slicing, rubbing, and sanding until it was a polished, sculptured shape.

Her energy seemed to have no limits. Mark teased, "Hey, Little Red Tornado, don't work so hard."

"But Mark, this isn't work. It's fun. Just like fixing up this loft was fun." Calling on all the techniques she had learned in her cold water walk-up; scraping, sanding, painting, patching, wiring, Emily had divided the 2,200 square feet of space into a mirror-walled dance studio, and a cozy apartment. "That's my recreation, Mark. It's a diversion from my dance work. It's fun."

"Some fun. But you couldn't do anything about the ceiling, could you?"

The ceiling was too low for spectacular high lifts. Only under the huge skylight, with the extra height, could they achieve the elevation they desired without cracking Emily's head. "People are going to notice that all our lifts come at the same place on-stage," Mark said.

"Not if we put some low lifts in other places. It's just another problem in choreography. More fun."

Emily was evolving her own choreographic methods and techniques. Her movement originated from a feeling, or dramatic idea. Often, starting with a series of apparently unrelated poetic images, she created a flowing sequence. The next stage was to hone and refine the sequence into more stylized movement defined by rhythm. Next it was shaped and formed into a theatrical idea, a story, with a singular, unifying style. Costumes, sets, and lighting concepts were added, and the work was rehearsed, further refined and polished, until its energy, its message and impact, reached beyond the studio, grew large enough to fill a theater.

By mutual agreement, because of her sense of organization, Emily was the main planner. She established carefully detailed schedules for their work time. Each session began with a barre. Next, time was spent rehearsing works essentially completed. Then came time to complete sections not yet formed. The evening was planned so that while Emily sewed costumes on her machine, Mark sawed and hammered and painted, building the sets. Finally, after a prescribed amount of time for household tasks, Emily returned to the typewriter to work on correspondence and the next day's schedule.

For a while her schedule called for the rehearsal of a solo depicting laughter. New York was in the midst of a heat wave, and the loft had no air conditioning. The dance sequence was dizzying, convulsive. For days in a row, she found that after fifteen minutes of rehearsal, she would have an unscheduled trip to the bathroom sink where she would vomit, then return and rehearse, be excused again, and so on into the early evening.

Yet she was in excellent physical condition. Working daily

with Mark, rehearsals with the Weidman and Graham companies, refined her, strengthened her. Still, she wasn't satisfied. She wanted to be stronger, more flexible, more articulate. After all, wasn't she about to embark on her own tour as the leading lady? Through that strenuous rehearsal period, filled with her Zephyr dream, the discipline she imposed on herself was that of a ballerina in a major company. Such dancers were making $500, $700, $1,000 a week, but with every point of their toe, every gesture, under the scrutiny of other dancers, ballet masters, choreographers, audiences.

She was her own ballet master, forcing herself to extremes of discipline. She would kneel on the floor, 20 minutes for each foot, supporting her weight on her toe joints and hands, so that the top of the arch would be stretched. Her hands, which the Weidman dancer had termed "awkward and inexpressive," became eloquent during long sessions in front of the mirror practicing the complex Hindu hand exercises that required even more articulation than deaf-and-dumb sign language. In front of the mirror she worked on her face, too, the way her eyes opened and how long they remained closed when blinked. She practiced willing her eyes not to blink for ten-minute spans, developing control of what is usually thought of as an involuntary reflex.

She practiced and perfected the facial mudra of the Indian dancer that she had learned from lessons at La Meri's school, and from photographs in library books. The facial mudra is a complicated set of exercises in which the practitioner learns to use and control the scores of tiny muscles in the face in order to express certain emotions. The lower lip, for example, must tremble to express fear; the worried eye slightly enlarges from the corners, drawn by muscles in the eyebrows and rim of the eyelid. The quivering cheek symbolizes one form of anxiety, the left nostril another, and the ears still another.

Emily experimented with her hair, slightly altering the color, sometimes eliminating or emphasizing the braids by adding more hair. She learned to be her own hairdresser, able to change character quickly by going from a bouffant Gibson Girl hairdo to an Old English pageboy, to a ponytail, to a gigantic Marie Antoinette pile of curls.

The "Little Red Tornado" attended dance concerts to learn. She was there to study details: programming—how to balance a program between humor and tragedy; length of intermission; the

77

different kinds of makeup and how each looked under stage lights; shoe technique—shape and color of the shoes, how they were fastened to the feet; color and texture of dance tights and the various ways of supporting them so they wouldn't wrinkle; audience reaction to different types of performers; and how curtain calls are taken in order to achieve the best audience response.

Watching her frenzied activity, Mark was helpless and amused. "Honestly, Emily, sometimes I think you manage to program thirty-six hours of activity into every day. Why do you drive yourself so?"

"Work is fun for me, Mark. My fun is work. I don't deliberately schedule constant activity, but I like using time and controlling it, not letting it slip away."

She repeatedly practiced a two-minute routine that consisted of a continuous sequence of dervish turns until she could do it without dizziness.

"Okay, but why do a routine you're never going to perform? Hindu dancers are trained from youth to do that, and you're not going into temple dancing."

She tried to explain. It was her hungry curiosity; when she saw someone else do a movement, she had to try that movement. "And my choreography is my school, my teacher. I give myself things to do that are technically beyond me. I enjoy the challenge. It's like learning languages. I learn by speaking, not studying the grammar. I'm trying to master more and more feats in dancing by doing them. The more difficult, the more dangerous, the better. It's like those lifts we do. You know I'm not an acrobat, but I do acrobatic lifts. If I examined them intellectually, I'd be frightened. But I just *do* them, with you."

There was a three-minute sequence of continuous jumps that she had practiced until she could do it with no appreciable loss of breath. Long and frequent repetitions trained her, at first, to obscure the luxury of panting for breath, and finally to never gulp air at all.

"I know those things cause you pain," Mark said. "What are you trying to prove?"

How could she explain her childhood commitment, her Zephyr dream? She was like a peasant who loves the earth, and keeps working the soil—not to make money, but to make things grow. Maybe simply because the peasant loves the act of tilling the soil. "All the things of my work—the monotonous things, the painful things, the dreary and routine things, and the dangerous challenges—I do them for the pleasure in the actions themselves, not to win or to get any prizes.

"I like the moment of *doing* best of all."

"But Emily, what about pain? How can you stand all of that pain you inflict on yourself?"

"Maybe I just have a high pain tolerance, Mark. I take each moment as it comes. Then go on. I try to understand the pain, the elements of the pain. Then I don't fear it. I relax into the pain, and breathe. Then somehow it's digested, incorporated into me, and though it still hurts, I can handle it."

Mark put the last touches on the set piece he was painting, laid the brush on the newspaper, and stood up. "Emily?"

"Hhmmmmm?" She was kneeling, stretching her arches, reading a magazine.

"I've been thinking, and—"

"Mark, I wish you wouldn't put the paintbrush on the newspaper. I haven't read it yet."

"Sorry." He picked up the offending brush, looked around for a more suitable resting place. "Anyway, I've been thinking, about us. I think we should—"

She turned another page of the magazine.

"Emily? Are you listening to me?"

"Sure, Mark. You've been thinking about us, and you think we should. You stopped there. Should what?"

"You sure do make it difficult. What I'm trying to say is—Emily! Get off your knees."

"Go ahead. I'm listening. I'm going for thirty minutes in the stretch. Got six minutes to go."

"Well, I'm not going to wait six minutes. By then I might be out of the mood. I think we should be . . . together, you know?"

"We *are* together, Mark. We're the Dance Drama Duo, or have you forgotten?"

"That's not what I mean. Oh, dammit, this is stupid! You

on your knees, and me upright with paint all over me. It's all wrong. Not the paint. It's not the way it's supposed to happen."

"The way what's supposed to happen?"

"A proposal."

She turned another page in the magazine.

"Emily! Didn't you hear me?"

"Mmm . . . hmmm." Encouragingly.

"I said I'm trying to propose. Marriage. I want to marry you."

Another page in the magazine was turned.

Exasperatedly: "Emily!!!"

She giggled.

"I want you to be my wife. It would make sense. I mean, when we're out touring. You know, hotel rooms and stuff. And after all, I've practically been living here for the last five months. . . ." His voice trailed off.

A flush was gradually spreading up from her neck into her face. She stared fixedly at the magazine, refusing to look at Mark. She laughed.

"Please don't laugh. I'm serious."

She suppressed her giggles and looked at him for the first time. "Oh, I know you're serious. It's just these positions we're in. Can you just see this scene? I thought we were supposed to be in a romantic setting—you know, a candle burning, soft music on the phonograph, me sitting on the couch, you on your knees at my feet, tenderly holding my hand, gazing deep into my eyes. . . ."

He laughed. "Dammit, in the first place, you don't have a couch—all you've got is orange crates nailed together. And the only music on the phonograph is music you're choreographing. I can't ever get you to sit still long enough for me to ask you properly. So I just . . . thought. . . ."

She was giggling again. "Mark, I love my orange crates. That's my first furniture, and I made it all myself. And sure, I put our dance music on the phonograph, but some of it is soft, romantic—"

He interrupted her. "Don't argue at a time like this. Will—you—marry—me? Well? Yes or no?"

Her voice softened. "Mark, you haven't mentioned love."

"You are the most frustrating woman I've ever met. Why

80

did I ever think of asking you to marry me? All I've been trying to tell you is that I love you. I want to marry you. I want to be your husband."

She smiled at him. "I really am sorry. It's just that I never thought about getting married. At least, not since I was a little girl."

"You're still a little girl, to me," he said tenderly.

"I'm underage. I'll have to get my parents' permission."

"But that'll take time. And won't they want to set up some big ceremony, with all your relatives and friends?"

"Yes, I suppose they will. Look, I'll fake it. I can get some I.D., a driver's license. We both need a driver's license."

"Oh, right. Well, we'll just go downtown tomorrow and get our licenses. And then—"

"We have to know how to *drive* first. I mean, that's important." Emily was being practical.

And she was laughing. "Mark, this is the silliest thing. You standing there with paint all over you, in your old khaki shirt and blue jeans, and me kneeling—I forgot! Is my half hour up yet?"

"Quite a while ago, I think."

She sat cross-legged on the floor, and looked at her watch. "Oh, look! I did thirty-three minutes. Can you believe it? That means tomorrow, I can try for—"

"Hey, wait a minute. We were talking about getting married. . . ."

She laughed again. "No, we were talking about learning to drive, in order to get a driver's license, in order to get our marriage license, in order to get married, in order to get what, exactly?" She finished on a quiet, serious note.

" . . . To be in love, Emily. To dance together and be a real couple. To make our dancing into real communication between two people. To be perfect. . . ."

"There's another thing, Mark. An important thing."

"What's that?"

"We have to get a car to tour, and we have to learn to drive it."

"Oh Emily, for God's sake!"

81

The newlyweds bought an ex-Checker cab—a big, reliable car with plenty of room for sets and costumes. The odometer said 90,000 miles, but Mark suspected the truth was closer to twice that. When the driver's door was closed, the engine sputtered, seemed about to start. The salesman assured them it was nothing to worry about. Anyway, his take-it-or-leave-it price of $400 was all they could afford.

"I just don't know if we did the right thing," Mark grumbled as they drove back to the loft building. "There's even a hole in the floorboard."

As the warm September air blew past their ankles, Emily said, "Look at it this way. We've got air conditioning, and it didn't cost us a dime."

The season's first snowstorm caught them in the hills of western Pennsylvania. The Checker's ancient heating system couldn't cope with the "air conditioning" in the floorboard. The defroster didn't work, and Emily had to wipe the inside of the windshield in front of Mark's eyes. "This way I've got an excuse to sit in the middle," his wife giggled. "It's actually cozy, kind of fun."

On the first long downhill stretch, the hood flew up, blocking Mark's view of the road. He managed to get safely to the shoulder, then got out, slammed the hood viciously, and kicked the fender. "Dammit."

"Let's name her," Emily suggested brightly. "I think . . . Cupid. Yes. As in Donder and Blitzen and Comet and Vixen. 'On, Cupid.'"

An hour later, as they were making their careful way along the icy highway, the engine stalled completely. "What do you think we ought to do now?" Mark asked. "Give it a kiss?"

"You know about things mechanical. Look under the hood."

The piece of steel that had sprung upward so readily as they drove downhill now refused to budge. Mark swore and kicked the grille. After two more kicks, the hood yielded.

Without benefit of flashlight, sleet soaking his back, Mark peered helplessly into the decrepit old car's mechanical innards.

Praying to the gods of random chance, swearing at the hot metal, he tinkéred with any part that moved. He climbed back in the car and pressed the button. The starter whined and whined, but the engine didn't budge.

Mark got out and squinted through the storm for approaching headlights. Emily sat huddled against the cold, thinking. Now which door was it? She emerged from the passenger side and slammed the door as hard as she could. Nothing happened.

"Emily, what are you doing?"

"Remember when the salesman slammed the car door, the engine started? Remember?"

"You've got to be kidding."

She walked around to the driver's side. Mark cursed a car that sped past, unheeding. She opened the door, slammed it shut. There was a protesting wheeze, a belch of black smoke from the rusted tailpipe, and the engine coughed to life.

"Quick," she called, "Jump in. Keep it going, before it stops again."

Mark did as he was told, nursed the engine to its version of a smooth purr. He glanced suspiciously at his wife. "I suppose you think now that you're an engineering genius."

She smiled serenely. "On, Cupid."

Hood flapping, engine stalling, door slamming, the Dance Drama Duo headed west.

A letter addressed to Harriet Schaeffer caught up with them. It was from the 92nd Street YMHA in New York, booking them for a one-night engagement in February. The 92nd Street Y was known as a showcase for dancers, its programs highly respected by both art world and critics. It would be Emily's New York debut.

Emily's preparations had started years before; now they only intensified. If the Y appearance was a personal Mount Everest, then the long tour through the winter-gripped Midwest was a time for perfecting skills on the approaches to the base camp. Her cue sheets became marvels of simplicity and accuracy that made the technicians' jobs easy. Her personal preparations became an unvarying routine, as precise as constant repetition could produce.

Exactly three hours before curtain time she would arrive at the theater, change into practice clothes, and set up her tape recorder and hand-carried metronome on the stage to take a barre. Next she would play the tapes of their program for the evening and do a thorough run-through, checking the stage for tiny variations in the floor, checking herself on the difficult passages in each of their dance works. Then she would go into her dressing room and carefully lay out bobby pins, hairpieces, costumes, and makeup. Each item was always in its assigned spot.

Finally, about ninety minutes before curtain time, she lay down wherever she could find an out-of-the-way corner—often on the bare floor—and allowed her mind to drift away from the details of the upcoming performance. She called it "zeroing out" or "disappearing," her way of resting, gathering strength for the evening.

As her personal routine became unvarying, so did the choreography. By the time she and Mark arrived in New York, their program was as finely tuned as their muscles.

The concert would open with "Sonata," a duet to light music which introduced the two dancers. Next came "Soliloquy," Mark's solo as Richard the Third. Then came Emily's solo, "Ballad of the False Lady": costumed in a magnificent velvet period dress, she danced the old English folk song of a young woman who kills her false lover. The two joined for "Haunted Moments," about how the sounds of everyday living compel people to act. They had tape-recorded ringing telephones, cash registers, the whistles and chuggings of trains, a clock ticking, people cheering, the sound of laughter.

After intermission, they would dance "Biblical Suite," in which Mark danced the Prophet Isaiah. Emily did "Hagar and the Angel," and they both danced "Jacob Loved Rachel." Their closing number, "People and Things," was a duet about a married couple moving into a house which they gradually fill with possessions until their relationship has no meaning and they are possessed by their possessions.

When they arrived at the Y for the tech rehearsal the day before the performance, they were told that the house was sold out. More people were clamoring for tickets than could possibly be accommodated. Every critic of note would be there, and many dance notables. Perhaps it was because Mark's was a major name in dancing, and the two had received excellent reviews during their tour, but also, the dance world was curious about the joining of a Graham dancer and a Weidman dancer.

The day of the performance, Emily arrived at the theater four hours early.

She took as much time as she could with her barre, with her run-through, and her bobby pin ritual. But her familiar routine could consume only so much time, no more. There was nothing for her to do but lie down in a quiet corner of the stage and let her mind ramble.

"You're a stepchild of genius," went her father's dialogue in her head. "People in our family always fail."

"But, Daddy, I haven't failed. Look at all the people who are coming to watch me dance tonight. And Mark and I have gotten wonderful notices on our tour."

"That's just a facade, Emily. You haven't been truly successful because the people you're competing with are inferior. That'll be proven tonight. You'll see."

She recalled the doctors, the foot specialists, who had surrounded her examining table. "This girl will never dance. Her feet are absolutely wrong for dancing." And the pain in her carefully bound and wrapped feet began to increase.

The scene at the Weidman studio came to mind. "The only reason people look at her is because she does the movements all wrong." "She hasn't got any technique. Her feet don't point. Stiff hands."

By the time Mark arrived, she was ready to go home. "I've never danced for the people in the dance world. What if they don't like me?"

"Emily, I've been through this for ten years. Once you start dancing, everything will be all right, believe me. You'll forget all about the people out there; all you'll be doing is dancing to music you know perfectly. And you know what we've created is good. People all over the country have loved it, and they're people who know dance, too."

In her opening costume at last, as she walked slowly to her spot to await the first curtain, her feet felt like lumps of cement. She was absolutely convinced that her muscles would not be able to support her weight. For the first time in her short career, she experienced nervous terror.

A surge of applause greeted them as the curtain went up. "We've heard great things about you," their peers were telling them, "and we're ready to love you." The nervousness was gone.

Mark and Emily soared. Their leaps were higher than ever before; their balances, extensions, turns, more dangerous—yet steadier—more exciting. They hit their lifts with a fierce élan.

After each number on their program, the storm of applause and bravos grew. At the final curtain, they could feel the physical force of the cheering.

Thirteen curtain calls later, they escaped to the dressing room. During the performance, the stagehands had filled it with bouquets of flowers and covered the walls with telegrams of encouragement and good wishes.

Emily didn't have a chance to get out of her costume or take off her makeup before the room was thronged with well-wishers who had come to share in the triumph. The backstage "performance" went on as long as the one on stage. Finally, Emily slumped at the dressing table, skimming the letters and telegrams.

There was a note from Sara, her sister in Harrisburg. Out of the envelope fell a scrap of paper, a picture torn from the pages of *Snip Snops*. Sara had penned, "Tonight, you were Zephyr."

7.
Indianapolis Hospital

"John, do you think the operation will work?"

He sighed, "Emily you've faced challenges all your life, and now you're facing another one. One of the things I love about you, you don't give in. And you won't this time, either."

Under his arm was a rolled-up *Time* magazine. "I picked this up in the airport. It's got an article I think you'll enjoy, about Makarova."

He handed her the magazine, opened to the picture of Natalia Makarova in the classic *penché arabesque*. She hardly glanced at it, dropped it idly on her nightstand.

"But do you think I'll be able to dance again?"

"That's what I'm talking about. This whole experience has been a blow. But you've got the courage and intelligence to make adversity work *for* you, not against you."

She reached for the magazine and its picture of Makarova. "Do you think I'll ever be able to do this?"

Music buffs know instinctively if an opera singer is off pitch, or a violinist misses a note. In classical dance the *penché arabesque* is one of the positions on which dancers are judged. A dancer's balance must be perfectly centered to execute the *penché*, for she stands on one leg, leaning far forward as if headed for a nose dive to the floor; her back is in a high arch; the other leg is turned out and extended toward the ceiling in a high straight line from the middle of her back, as close to 180 degrees—a perfect split—as she can manage. The high arch, the split leg, are maintained by her body's invisible strengths—balance and years of practice.

Emily wondered, would she still have those "invisible strengths"? Could she achieve a high arched back like that with a spinal fusion?

"Darling, I think you'll be able to do anything you set your mind to," John was saying. "And knowing your mind, yes, I think so."

Emily glanced at the clock, began consuming the minutes. I want the time to go by faster, faster, she thought, I want to get to sleep and then it'll be morning—I'll be on my way to surgery and I can start healing and working and heading for home.

John grinned. "You're clock-watching again, Em. As long as you're going to be timekeeper around here, let me know when ten minutes are up. I'm on my honor to get out of here in ten minutes. Your head nurse is getting tough. I think she means it this time."

A nurse appeared in the doorway. "Sir, your time is up."

As John bent to kiss Emily, her eyes sought his again. "Em, I'm sure that it'll go all right. I'll be here tomorrow when you come back from Recovery."

Dr. Sam bounced into her room. "Hello, there, small lady," He grinned. "What's new in your rather limited world?"

"Hi, Dr. Sam," she smiled. "Or is it Dr. Hugh? Sometimes I just can't keep it straight. Depends on what kind of mood you're in. You never told me how you got two first names."

Briefly, he related his story of adoption by an uncle whose Americanized name was "Sam."

"But what about the 'Hugh'?"

"Well, my given name was Hu-Hua." His pronunciation of the Chinese syllables started her giggling.

"When you're being a Jewish mother to me, you're Dr. Sam. Hugh is such an Anglo-Saxon name, so when you're being a serious, intellectual medical expert, I think of you as Dr. Hugh."

"Well, I'm here as Dr. Hugh. I want to make sure you're not worrying overmuch about tomorrow."

"The only thing I could worry about is that you might not be telling me everything." He didn't answer. "I know that Dr. Morrison says there's only a fifty-fifty chance of success. My husband told me."

"I'm concerned about your physical condition, Emily. It'll be a long operation, and you're pretty weak."

"Do you think I might die? I'm aware of that risk."

"We could still cancel the operation."

"Doctor, when I was a little girl, I promised God that I would never quit dancing 'until death do us part.' I'm a grown woman now, and I know what that vow means, and I know what death is. If the operation fails and I die, or I'm crippled—well, it's not a child's view any more. It's an adult's decision."

Dr. Sam replied, "All right. I'm satisfied that your mental attitude is healthy. And I know that Dr. Morrison is one of the most skilled neurosurgeons in the country. We've studied your charts and X rays thoroughly and settled on a procedure that offers you the best chance at recovery. We don't know the extent of damage to your spinal cord, but the evidence we have now indicates that we will be able to restore movement to your lower body."

Dr. Sam described the operation. First, the team of doctors would remove the bone splinters and fragments from the area of the break. If callus had already formed, it would be removed. Next, a surgeon would remove a segment of bone from her hip and use it to splint the break in her back, where it would serve as the foundation for new bone formation. After the hip resection, the doctors would realign her broken back, finally insert the hipbone, and wire the splint together. Neurosurgical techniques would repair as much nerve damage as possible. And lastly, all the torn tendons, ligaments, and muscle tissue would be sewn back together.

"You say the fusion will be wired together." she considered. "Won't the wires come out eventually, like stitches?"

89

"No. We use stainless surgical wire. It's a permanent procedure—the wires will be with you the rest of your life."

Later, after he left her room, she thought about all the things she had learned. What if an athlete had to spend a full year out of action? Would he be able to come back? I'm an athlete, too, and a year is a long time.

Emily thought of the past year's work to get back into condition after three years without performing. But I took a barre nearly every day during those three years, she reminded herself, and never really got out of shape. Now she was facing a year on her back—a year in a cast and brace—a year just learning to walk again.

Yes, she decided: If her sentence was a year, then she would serve the sentence, be a good patient, the best there ever was. But a year only, no more; for that was borderline.

Her mainspring was starting to wind again, the mainspring all dancers wind overtight to drive them through their grueling discipline. She pictured herself executing the *penché arabesque* perfectly. It was her trick from healthier days—mental rehearsal of a position or choreography was relaxing.

The anesthetist paid her a late visit to explain the type of anesthesia he would use, ordered her to eat nothing after midnight.

"And please prescribe a good strong sleeping pill for me." Tonight of all nights, she didn't want the long sleepless hours, filled with the madness of two arguing voices, the dread and uncertainty about her future.

And then came Dr. Morrison, late, just before lights out. She wished fervently to be left alone to prepare herself for the battle, to sleep quickly and deeply until they came to get her in the morning.

But Dr. Morrison was opening his little black kit and asking her questions that required concentration.

"Last time for the feathers and needles?" she asked.

"If all goes well tomorrow, I probably won't be needing these for you."

"What do you mean, 'If all goes well . . .'? Please don't tell me you have doubts."

"A spinal fusion procedure is very complicated and very delicate," he answered. "On the other hand, I've done quite a few of these. And, if I may say so myself, been pretty successful. I think we'll have you on your feet and walking again—if we can restore feeling to your lower body."

90

She was concentrating hard now, analyzing every word. "Do you think there's a chance you may *not* be able to restore feeling?"

"Of course, there's always a *chance* a surgical procedure won't work out exactly as expected. But you mustn't concern yourself with chances. I could quote you all the old clichés about walking across the street or riding in cars.

"In my professional opinion, the chances of success in tomorrow's operation are good. And that's the positive thought you must keep in your mind."

"All right, I understand what you're telling me. And I've got reinforcement from Dr. Sam. He's optimistic about my operation tomorrow, and I'll be walking in a year." She went on to describe what she knew of the recovery period—the cast, then the brace, a wheelchair, crutches, and finally taking steps on her own. She wanted to prove what she knew of physical therapy, demonstrate her eagerness to be a good patient, to do everything this stern father-figure recommended.

Dr. Morrison was silent, his back turned, staring out at the bleak landscape, cloaked in the gray shades of late winter. When she paused for a breath, he said quietly, "It may take five years."

Like a tiny mouse, her mind scurried this way and that, seeking escape from the trap he had sprung. Morrison had condemned her to five years before she would regain sufficient use of her legs. There would be no appeal.

His next words confirmed it: A one-year prognosis was unrealistic. Certainly, there was always the chance that the recovery period could be less. But he insisted she be realistic, and realistically, she should plan on five years.

Then she was alone in the room. It seemed suddenly cold. All energy, hope, was slipping away. She didn't know how to stop it; couldn't understand why this was happening to her.

There would be no more dancing, then. No barres, no jumps, no arabesques, *penché* or otherwise. No choreography. Never again would she feel the excitement of a *pas de deux,* two bodies moving distinctly, yet as one in perfect harmony. Never again to fly. And to replace those elements of her life, to replace her life itself?

"Oh, Zephyr," she called softly. "I've lost you." Emily, who had not "winced or cried aloud," now reached out for help. She

91

called to the head nurse passing in the hall. "Please . . . I'm afraid. The doctor said the recovery period might take a long, long time."

"Well now, you just lie back and rest," the nurse answered. "You've got two of the best surgeons in Indiana. They're going to take good care of you. There's time enough to worry about the recovery when it's all over."

"Can I have a sleeping pill?"

"But you're not due a pill for another thirty minutes. Don't you want to wait like you usually do?"

Emily, who had so carefully hoarded her resources in the battle against pain, now spent them recklessly. "No. I'm afraid. Please just give me the pill. I don't want to think anymore. I want to go."

A male nurse, with whom she had lightly bantered to cover the embarrassment she felt when he emptied her bedpan, poked his head in the room. "Well, I hear you're off to surgery in the morning. Finally going to get out of your torture rack? You'll do fine, I know it.

"Hey." He picked up the *Time* magazine opened to the picture of Makarova's *penché arabesque*. "I'll bet that looks just like you. What a wonderful pose." He held out the open magazine.

Emily grabbed it and hurled it away with as much strength as her limited motion allowed.

But later that night, John was again back at his wife's side at the hospital. He had managed to come into her room at 1:30 A.M. The nurses at the desk had phoned him and reported that she was restless, unable to sleep, upset.

"I can't help it. I can't live if it's five years, John."

"Em, your only chance is to make yourself believe that it isn't going to be five years. The surgery is tough enough for your body to endure without you going into it in a negative, defeated frame of mind. That's why you have to take the insecurity. You don't know how long it will take. But you are *not* better off dead. Your only chance to survive this surgery successfully is for you to go in there fighting and determined to live and to get back on your feet in the shortest time possible."

"But how, John, how? I don't believe it."

"You know how. We both know how. That's our work. That's what makes us good artists and honest performers. You bring

92

every ounce of your artistic self, the one who can conjure up moods of joy, of passion, of fear—on the stage—and bring that self right here. And you conjure up, right here and now, a conviction that you can handle it, that you want to survive, that you will survive."

"Yes. . . . 'No matter how straight the gate. . . .' "

"The Poem."

"Yes. The Poem. Okay, I can do it. I can at least try, John. I will try."

"Fight it," she murmured aloud.

She was back, standing in her childhood living room, shoulders square, head high, pigtails swinging, reciting for her father, "I have not winced, nor cried aloud. Under the bludgeonings of chance, my head is bloody, but unbowed. . . ."

She was following John's instructions, drowning out the voice that wanted to die.

". . . I am the master of my fate. I am the captain of my soul."

I won't go to sleep, she thought. I won't take another pill. If it takes all night, I'll stay awake and fight.

And then she was drifting on a cloud of sedation. The morning sun shown through the treetop outside the window, casting dancing shadows on the ceiling. The hum of electronic equipment blended with the chatter of the public address system into a symphonic chord.

"Listen," she whispered, waiting for the surgical attendants to come for her. "Can you hear it? Music—majestic music."

As the surgical cart was wheeled down the corridor, the grim face of Dr. Morrison appeared above her. "Don't be so glum," she laughed. "You were wrong, Daddy."

The face stayed starkly serious. I'll make him smile now, she thought, as the double doors of the operating theater swung wide. I'll lift my leg in the most beautiful arabesque ever.

Gentle hands lifted her onto the operating table, turning her face down. "That's a pirouette," she whispered. "A clockwise adagio. See my lovely turn, Mark? I'm turning . . . turning. . . ."

8.

Dance Drama Company

"Could I take class with you sometime?" asked the young girl who had watched Emily and Mark's performance at the Y. By the time the pair left New York to resume their tour, they had collected a small group of disciples who assembled each day to study the technique that was rapidly evolving as Emily's own.

Two weeks later, back on the road, a letter arrived from Mark's mother containing clippings from the reviews of their Y concert. Walter Terry of the New York *Herald Tribune* wrote: "He is big, strong and handsome. She is little, lithe, utterly lovely, reminds one of the great Doris Humphrey in her dancing days. . . ." Before Mark could finish reading one review, Emily would interrupt with one even better.

"Oh, Mark, these are rave reviews! They loved us."

Sputtering down the Pennsylvania Turnpike in their taxicab, the two played future games. "I can see it all now," Mark chuckled. "When we finish this tour, there'll be people lined up in New York wanting us to do a season."

Emily picked up, "We could have a run on Broadway, really, like a big company. Can't you just see the marquee, in big letters—'RYDER AND FRANKEL. The Dance Drama Duo . . . Eight weeks' limited engagement.' . . ."

"I've got a better idea. How about 'The Dance Drama Company'? Then the big letters: 'Starring EMILY FRANKEL and MARK RYDER.' You can be billed first. I'm a gentleman."

"A company? That's too much."

"No, look, I'm serious. I've wanted to form a company for a long time, but I never told anybody. I guess I never had the right opportunity."

Though Mark had achieved distinction and renown as the Graham company's leading male dancer, he had never been able to implement his idea of combining dance and drama. Now, teaming with Emily, he had his chance. With their success at the Y, they had broken into the dance world's inner circle. With their newly-acquired reputation, they had the basis to form a major company.

"We can have a touring company, just like Martha and Weidman's," he continued, "only bigger—thirty dancers, maybe more. We can do much more than either of them. We'll have a New York season every year, and a major national tour. We could even go to Europe."

"Just four more dancers," Emily mused. "If we start small, it wouldn't be a financial problem. We can expand later on." The idea was appealing.

"And we've already got the students who have been taking class with us," Mark added. "Anya is certainly good enough. And she's enthusiastic. And Jerry, he's a hard worker, and he's got a lot of potential."

If they had their own company, Emily realized, she would grow. Her own choreography would increase in scope, her movement range would improve in a competitive situation. "You're right, Mark. It's our next major artistic step."

Getting the dancers for their new company was easy. Of some 5,000 professional modern dancers in New York, perhaps only 100 were employed full-time at their chosen profession. From this huge pool of young talent, Mark and Emily chose two boys and two girls.

96

Organizing the company and its tours was simply a matter of expansion. Typewriter hours doubled because the letters were longer, but two part-time typists were hired. Press materials and brochures were bigger and better and more costly, so the increased financial responsibilities were handled through more installment arrangements. Higher fees would be charged. Emily, who had been working fourteen hours a day, easily managed sixteen, sometimes eighteen. As her brain evolved expanded concepts, her energies expanded as well. Less sleep was not a problem.

Mark asked, "What time did you finally come to bed last night?"

"About five. But I'm as fresh as if I had eight hours' sleep. I was sitting at the typewriter, about four A.M. I guess, doing the press book. I'd done another three hundred letters, and I kept wondering why I wasn't tired. My mind was kind of wandering, you know, but purposefully.

"I was thinking about what I was writing, of course, but at the same time I was thinking about the design of our costumes and how to make them, and how to use that D-minor chord in the 'Biblical Suite' adagio, and how to fix that scheduling problem between Albuquerque and Tucson. My mind was working in several different directions at once, and not just fantasizing, either. I was holding all those different threads of constructive thought, all at the same time. That's the first time in my life I ever experienced anything like that. It felt as if my brain started using more cylinders or went into overdrive. Has anything like that ever happened to you?"

He shook his head ruefully. "No."

"When I realized what was happening, I started trying to do it on purpose. And I could *keep* doing it. It's like carrying on a conversation with somebody and at the same time solving math problems in your head. I think I can use it, make it work for me like a new tool. I'm going to practice it, learn to do it at will."

"You do that." Mark shrugged his shoulders at his wife, her enthusiasm bubbling out all over, engulfing his life. It certainly did make it easier, he thought, to have someone like her around, working on problems, no matter what crazy way she did it.

Mark felt that simply re-choreographing their present repertory for four more dancers would get them started as a group. Emily wanted more. "Let's have outside choreographers. We'll select the music and give them ideas and librettos so that our dance drama concept will continue. How exciting to have an outside choreographer give me movement. You've already experienced that, but I haven't. I need it to develop as a soloist."

"But won't that be awfully expensive?"

"It can't hurt to ask some choreographers. We'll offer them a small fee, plus a small royalty. Let's try."

They compiled and contacted a list of choreographers. Intrigued by Emily's librettos and choice of music, several agreed to work with the Dance Drama Company. Weidman did a soap opera spoof, "Penelope Is Pursued." Sophie Maslow, Artistic Director of the New Dance Group, produced "Diamond Backs" about a teenage gang. Hadassah, a noted ethnic dancer, did "Fairy Tale" in Hindu style. Todd Bolender, soloist and choreographer for Balanchine's New York City Ballet, created his ballet "Still Point," later performed by ballet companies around the world.

They bought a new station wagon on time payments, designed new sets. "Harriet Schaeffer" continued to serve as press agent and company manager, handling the multitude of travel and booking details. Emily danced, rehearsed, and worked on the costumes with a seamstress from the fringes of the theatrical world who didn't charge them too much.

The little group worked through the spring and summer and by autumn were ready for their four-month cross-country tour: sixty-three one-night stands, five three-performance weekends, and two one-week residencies at colleges where they would also teach classes and run seminars for the dance and drama students. Overall, the results were more than encouraging. Consistently rave reviews were clipped and pasted in the scrapbook. The tour grossed $40,000, a profit of about $10,000, which Emily and Mark plowed right back into the kitty for new works, better sets, better costumes, higher salaries, and a large new van. And they began to pay their dancers rehearsal pay, unprecedented in the concert field, of $45 a week.

But the schedule was exhausting, with its full complement of dingy motels, greasy french fries, overdone hamburgers and underdone vegetables, flat tires, broken radiators, misplaced props, four fallings-out, three threats to quit the company, two fistfights, one bout with the flu. Despite "Harriet Schaeffer's" best efforts, many of the one-night stands were linked by long miles of night driving. And trouble between Mark and Emily suddenly surfaced.

After a performance at a Kansas school and the reception at the dean's home, Emily went back to the motel, sat in bed, ever-present notebook propped on her knees, giving herself notes from the evening's performance.

She awoke when Mark came in, tripping over a chair in the dark. "Hi," she called. "The reception get any better after I left?"

"Hell, no. If anything, it got even more boring."

"Didn't look like you were so bored," she said, laughing, "talking to the dean's daughter in that corner all evening."

"So what if I did. You jealous?"

"Wait a minute, I was just teasing. I don't care who you talk to in a corner—as long as talk is all you do."

"You don't seem to care about much of anything these days."

Her light mood evaporated, and suddenly she was fully awake. "What's that supposed to mean?" But he only shook his head morosely.

"Mark, I think you've got something on your mind. Why don't you tell me and get it over with so I can go to sleep. I'm really tired."

"I *know* you're tired. It shows in your dancing."

"What?"

"I said, it shows. In your dancing. Is that clear enough for you?"

Her eyes went cold.

"Emily, I'm serious. You lost the focus in that series of turns in 'Fairy Tale' tonight. You know the one, in the second movement? It was obvious to everybody. And in your promenade turns in 'Penelope,' you were so unsteady I thought you were going to fall."

"Is that all?"

"I don't think your concentration is what it used to be. 'Still Point' is still lacking something, it's just not getting across. And you being so tired makes it even worse."

"What do you think I should do about it?"

"I don't really know. Maybe stop working so hard, take a rest or something. Maybe go back to New York and take a couple weeks' vacation. Anya knows your roles; she could dance them."

"You'd like that, wouldn't you?" she responded acidly. "Get me out of the way for a while and leave you a clear field with Anya?"

"Oh, hell, that's not what I meant at all. I just think—"

"That's what you *implied*. And I don't care what you think. Now let's drop this subject before it gets dangerous, go to sleep. We've got to teach classes in the morning."

"I'm going to take a walk." He stalked out.

A week later, in South Bend, Indiana, Anya was sitting with Mark in a hotel coffee shop. She glanced at Emily, by herself at another table. "What's the matter with her lately?" Anya asked.

"You mean our Fearless Leader?"

"I guess so. She's been so quiet lately, hardly talks to anybody."

"Oh, she's just not as good as she thinks she is," Mark answered.

"I'm not so sure of that, Mark. She's a marvelous dancer. Look at her in 'Still Point.' That's such a beautiful dance, and she does it with such power. It gets more curtain calls and bravos each time we do it."

"Bolender did that dance for me, too, you know. She lets everybody think he did it just for her."

"Come off it; everybody knows you're in the dance, too. You're just edgy. It's been a long tour, and now we're on the home stretch. In a couple of weeks we'll be back in New York."

"That seems like forever. I don't know if I can keep dancing with Emily. Everybody thinks she's so great, but she makes mistakes like everybody else."

That night, as Mark lowered Emily to the floor from their most spectacular lift in 'Still Point,' her tender feet cracked against the floor. She had to fight for balance.

"Mark," she commented as they left the theater that night, "you almost dropped me tonight. What happened?"

"I didn't 'almost drop you.' You're the one who lost your balance."

100

"Come on, I wouldn't have lost my balance if you hadn't dropped me."

"That's what I've been talking about," he burst out. "It's never your fault, is it? Always somebody else's."

After the next performance, Emily didn't get her usual bravos. "Mark, what's the matter?" she asked him later. "I mean, with you and me? That's two nights in a row you nearly dropped me, and in the arabesque you made me reach so far for you I couldn't get my leg up."

"You know you always have trouble with a raked stage."

"Mark, I worked out on that stage two hours this afternoon. I always factor in a raked stage. Tell me what's wrong. We'll try to rehearse it."

"Rehearsing! That's your solution to everything." Mark walked off in a huff.

The next afternoon in tech rehearsal, Mark stopped abruptly and called out to the lighting technician. "Give me a follow-spot right here, on the jump series."

"But Emily's cue sheet doesn't have a follow spot here."

"I don't give a damn about Emily's cue sheet. I said *I* want a follow spot here."

"But Mark," Emily interrupted quietly, "we agreed that a follow spot anywhere in this number would ruin the effect."

"You're just trying to keep me in the dark," he shouted back. "This is one of my best places in the damn duet, and you want to make sure nobody sees me."

"That's not true."

"Of course it is! The whole company knows it." He was still shouting. "You upstage all of us with your clever little technical tricks."

"But—"

"And while we're on the subject of the company, we're picking up a nice profit from this tour, and you're putting it all into the company's new works. Well, I'm damn tired of sleeping in fleabag motels. Why can't we spend a little more, maybe split the pot with more money for us?"

"Mark," she replied, tight-lipped, "the tour's almost over. The time to make budget changes for next year is when we get home. Right now, we're holding up the rehearsal. And the longer we delay, the less rest we get before the curtain."

That night, after another ragged performance, Emily sought out Anya. "Am I just dreaming, or is Mark deliberately trying to disrupt things?"

"I don't know what's wrong, Emily, but I *do* know that something is bothering Mark!"

"I'm glad to know it's not just my imagination," Emily replied. "You've seen what's been happening to us on stage?"

"Sure. Everybody else has, too."

At their final stop before heading home, the performance was even worse. On their lifts, Mark gripped her flesh too hard. In her supported turns, she had to fight for balance. At the curtain call his hold on her hand was cruel, cutting off the circulation.

Heading for their dressing rooms, she stopped him. "All right! This is enough. I don't care about you and me. But I do care about the company. We've all got something good going here, and you're jeopardizing all of us with your childish behavior."

"That's all I hear—company, company, company. You think you run this company, but it's not yours alone, you know. Who do you think gave you all the ideas? Me, that's who."

"So the truth finally comes out," she answered evenly. "If I hadn't pushed, it wouldn't have gotten done. Sure you did a lot of work. But if I hadn't nagged you when you wanted to take a nap or take a couple days off, even that wouldn't have gotten done. . . ."

"It's a damn good thing this is the last performance," Mark shouted, gesturing angrily. "Because if it weren't, I'd make it the last one."

His gesture turned into a sweeping, fist-clenched punch that landed, with an audible crack, on her face.

Emily reeled and fell heavily to the floor. The other dancers gathered around her, Mark stormed into the dressing room, gathered up his belongings, and left without removing his makeup. When the company had finished packing and returned to the hotel, they discovered that Mark had already checked out and taken a bus to New York.

When she returned to the city, Emily checked into a hotel

102

instead of returning to the loft apartment. The next day she called home.

"Emily, I'm so sorry about everything. We have to talk. When are you coming home?"

She came in to discover Mark packing his bags.

"Emily, it's not right that you live in a hotel and I live here. This has been your home since before I came, so I'll be the one to move out. I've been thinking a lot since the other night—about us, the company, me. First of all, I want to apologize. I can't excuse what I did; all I can say is that I've never felt such frustration. It just kept building and building."

"But why didn't you say something, just *talk* to me? Instead of—"

"You know I've never been one to talk much, Emily. That's a problem I'm going to have to work on. And when you get really focused on a situation, as you were on our tour, you're not the easiest person in the world to talk to."

"It *was* a good tour, wasn't it? Everything worked out the way we planned."

"Yes, and the company's going to get even better, the way *you* planned it. For me, that's the biggest problem. It was your tour all along. Not that I couldn't do more. It's just that you did it all so much better and faster than I could. That's why I wanted to get away from Martha Graham. You're both high-powered women. I need to be the leader, the boss."

"But what will you do?"

"I'm thinking about teaching in a college. The academic life appeals to me, and it would give me time to work on my own things."

"But the company belongs to us both."

"You take it, Emily. I'll just take my share of what we made this year, and you take the costumes, sets, choreographies, the van, all the assets."

"Mark, we have that residency in Tennessee coming up."

"I'll come down and help out. But I'll come on my own. I've got to get out of the company."

"And the marriage, too, I guess?"

"You know, Em, marriage and a company are a lot alike. They both take cooperation, and for all the same reasons I mentioned about working with you in the company, I feel we should break, too. Listen, I'm not an evil man. About last week, that stuff backstage—" He took a deep breath. "Well, I'm sorry."

The town in Tennessee was a little Swiss jewel set down amid the gray-green grandeur of Tennessee's hills. A drive up the mountain, winding past condominium chalets for the wealthy, offers vistas of the Great Smokies. Emily felt content for the first time in years.

Things were, at last, going so nicely. The company was dancing well; Mark was there, choreographing. He, too, seemed content; Emily remained in the background. For this last time when they would work together, they had discovered a melancholy peace. Mark would soon leave for the fall semester at a college in New England; for her part, it was a time for rest, gathering energy for the demands of New York and a major national tour that winter.

Almost by accident she had found the little overlook, an outcropping of rock hidden from the road by a screen of trees. In her free moments she liked to go there to sit alone and contemplate. But now some people were coming through the trees from the road behind her. She glanced over her shoulder in irritation. To her relief it wasn't a bunch of noisy tourists, just three of the actors from the show. The tall blond man in the middle recognized her and waved diffidently. "Look's like this spot's already taken," he said to his friends. "Let's find another one on up the road." Before turning back through the trees, he smiled at her.

How nice, she thought. He seemed to understand that I need to be alone, that he and his friends would be intruding. He had the lead in the play. He was a good actor, and his voice filled their outdoor theater. I wonder what brought him here, she thought. Then she didn't think about him anymore.

But after the performance that night, there was a knock on her dressing room door. "Hi, Emily? Hope we didn't disturb you up on the mountain this afternoon."

"Oh, hi, John . . . No, as a matter of fact. . . ."

"Well, can I buy you a drink, or something? How about a walk down the main street? Mingle with the tourists a little. Window shop? We can stop for a cup of coffee."

"I could use a cup of coffee. Okay, I'll be ready in a few minutes." She surprised herself; usually she preferred to return to her room to give herself notes. Why had she agreed to go out? Well, he was handsome, and talented, and almost shy. Compared with all the men she knew in New York, that was appealing. And here was a chance to talk to a talented performer whose background must be so totally different from her own.

What a difference it was.

He had grown up in eastern Tennessee, son of one of the city's prominent businessmen, graduated from the university, served with the Army in Korea, and returned home to enter his father's business.

"But I didn't really want my whole life programmed," he told her. "I wanted to take some chances, do something on my own. So last spring I went into my father's office and told him I was quitting, auditioned for the play, and here I am."

Emily's background fascinated him. She had done all the things he had wanted to do—left home as a child, made her own way in New York, achieved national success and recognition as an artist.

"I'm getting a late start, but when this run is over, I'm going to New York and get a cheap little apartment, probably starve for a while, hit all the auditions. Maybe you can give me some names and contacts, or something. Do you mind if I call you?"

She wouldn't mind at all. He was a refreshing person, with an honesty and a drive that she recognized in herself. For the remainder of their time with the show, the two shared the mountain lookout, coffee, cast parties, long walks, and long talks.

The phone rang in her New York loft. "Hi, Emily. It's John. I'm here."

"Where's here?"

"Here in New York. Got a little studio apartment, and

well, not a job exactly, but it could lead to some things. I'm doing volunteer work for a repertory company."

Ambitious and full of energy, they got together. They quickly discovered that their individual talents blended perfectly. John's intuitive sense of music and drama helped shape and polish Emily's dance ideas. She helped him to break through into areas of emotion he would rather not have explored. They were growing in their respective fields, because of their influence on each other.

So gradually that it was a fact before either of them had made a conscious decision, John was living in the loft. They pooled his paychecks and her roller-coaster bank account, and decided that it made the most sense to get married.

Through their first year of marriage, she worked to pay off the company's debts she had inherited when Mark left, and built the company into a group some critics considered a potentially major dance company.

She enlarged the repertory, increased the number of dancers, booked major theaters around the country, including a European tour. John approved. "You've taken your company into the small towns and colleges which otherwise would have little or no exposure to art. Modern dance companies have always confined themselves to New York and the major cities—until you."

But Emily complained. "Sometimes it all seems like just too much work. I'm tired of being company manager, tour director, bus driver, mother and father, lead dancer, choreographer, booking agent, press agent, and janitor.

"Sometimes I don't feel I'm always close enough to the people in the company. I have to be the director, but I want them to like me, too. Is it possible?"

"That's the problem in theater companies," John said. "Can the director be friends with people he may have to fire? Being the boss is never the way to win popularity contests."

"All I've ever wanted to do was dance. All this extra company business that I have to do is taking too much time."

"Can you cut back a little? Let somebody else take the company out on the road. You stay home and just work on your dancing."

"I've had an idea, John, lately, about a new dance I want to do. It's not solid enough to talk about yet, but I think you're right.

106

We've got seven weeks on the road. I'll think about my idea, talk to you about it in my letters."

When Emily called after the performance in Carbondale, Illinois, John didn't answer. Understandable—he was probably rehearsing late. Neither was he home when she called from Des Moines. She had been on the road for a week. He probably went out to see a play, or to the corner pub with some friends. Nor was he home when she called from Bozeman, Montana.

The following week she called at noon.

"John! Where have you been? I've been worried."

"Your voice sounds funny," he said. "Are you okay, Emily?"

"It's nothing, John. The company is fine, the tour is fine. I'm getting good reviews, we're making money. My only problem is that I miss you. And when I call and you're not home. . . ."

"But Emily, I can't just sit home and wait for the phone to ring. I never know when you're going to call, or even if—"

"Of course. We can't plan definite phone times ahead. I never know when I'm going to be able to call. You know me, I just get these funny things in my mind. Anyway, there's something important I need to talk through with you."

"What is it?"

"For three years the company has been doing practically the same repertory in the same small colleges and towns. We're not progressing. And the main thing is, *I'm* not progressing. Harriet Schaeffer has become more important than my artist self."

"That sounds like you're thinking of disbanding the company."

"Not disband. Take a new direction. I've been thinking about my idea for a new dance every day on the tour. It'll be a huge commitment, might take me a year of rehearsals in New York. No touring. It's about dancers and their dreams."

Work on "Dream Dances" began. After interviewing each of the dancers, finding out how they'd felt about dancing as children, and what had led up to their dancing careers, Emily had

107

recorded the answers in a notebook and translated them into a choreographic plot.

Money to pay the company for a nine-month rehearsal period was borrowed. She commissioned three composers to write original music for "Dream Dances," hired a set designer and a costume designer, and booked the 92nd Street YMHA for two premiere performances. Emily would have preferred a larger theater, but such spaces booked far in advance would cost perhaps half their $10,000 budget. Waiting for more money and better space would be risky—the dancers could lose their energy or interest, perhaps find other work.

For the nine months, the eight dancers became her family. There were strange foodstuffs in her refrigerator, bodies napping on her couch or bed, people in her bathroom, kitchen, living room, office.

Two weeks before the opening, the final orchestra performance tapes were delivered. But the rhythms, pitch, and harmonic emphasis were different from the rehearsal tapes. Some of the costumes needed re-working. Some set pieces were too cumbersome. But there wasn't time to re-do, re-work, or re-record. "Dream Dances" had to be finished.

Eight dancers; eight separate stories; eight solos. As each company member danced his or her own solo, the other seven danced supporting roles, until it was their "dream's" turn.

"This is the best work I've ever done, John," she bragged one evening just before the Y. "It's my statement. I love it."

There was no break-in, just the two performances. The critics' reviews were damning. The idea had merit, they said, but the execution fell short. The stage was too crowded with props and set pieces—too gimmicky. The work was too long.

"Well, I guess my Daddy was right," she muttered to John, half facetiously, half in earnest. "I'm a failure and a stepchild of genius again." John tried to point out that some critics had liked her concept, others had praised her dancing, but she wouldn't listen.

Her way of healing was to accept that lack of preparation, carelessness, or a simple lack of experience—whatever had gone wrong—was totally her fault, while going on to the next project.

"John, guess it's time to put on my Harriet Schaeffer hat again. I feel like disbanding the company, but I won't. Harriet is going to send us all out on tour again to perform all the old familiar stuff from the repertory.

Emily decided that she would re-work and rebuild "Dream Dances" while she was on the road. With notebook and pencil and silent concentration she studied the piece's weaknesses. Also, she analyzed that she had panicked about money and time. That won't happen again. We'll re-mount it, try it out on the road. Then when we come in with it, we'll be ready. The failure won't be repeated.

"Of course, I'll hate being away from you again, John." Her tone became light, bantering. "It's a five-week tour. I'll make all those phone calls to you after performances, and you won't answer, I'll bet. Probably out with some cute little actress, I know."

"Oh Emily—" he started to protest.

"John, that's just me. You know, silly me with all my suspicions."

The work was good therapy. Meanwhile, the Harriet Schaeffer bookings for their first European tour were finalized. "Dream Dances" would premiere in Edinburgh, Scotland, then move on to London.

The company, now ten members, flew to Edinburgh. The old theater's raked stage was full of splinters and bumps—and was long and narrow, necessitating last minute changes in choreography. The lights were excellent, though gels had a tendency to fall off at the most inopportune moments. Autumn's damp chill seeped through the walls, cramping dancers' muscles. Demoralized at the conditions, the less dedicated new members of the group resorted to marijuana and alcohol. And a strange love affair had captured the company's attention. Jerry, a homosexual, had decided he was in love with Anya.

But such was Emily's excitement at dancing in Europe, her joy and satisfaction with the new "Dream Dances," that the company's problems were ignored.

After opening night, the company was hailed with the highest praise. The Edinburgh critics raved about "Dream Dances."

"A work of genius," they wrote. "This work will take its place alongside Martha Graham's 'Diversion of Angels,' Jerome Robbins' 'Opus Jazz' and 'Age of Anxiety.' Frankel has created a masterwork." But despite the success, the company was seething with grievances, gossip, and bad humor.

In London, after a long day of rehearsals, Anya came to Emily's hotel room.

"You know, everybody in the company thinks I'm freaked out. Jerry's gay, everybody knows that. But they don't understand him, not like I do. I can get inside his head. And he says he loves me. Now everybody's saying terrible things."

Emily said, "Anya, if you like him, and he likes you, that's your business. Don't worry about what other people think."

"But Emily, I don't really know if I love him or not. I was sort of going with Hans, too, and well—I just don't know how to handle it."

"I'm not your mother, Anya."

"But you've been married and divorced. You've been through this sort of thing. You're the only one I can talk to. And I . . . I missed my period."

"Hans or Jerry?"

Anya shrugged. "Or Douglas—we had a thing going for a little while. And if Jerry ever finds out, he'll kill me. Or Hans. And if I'm pregnant. . . ."

"Anya," Emily said quietly, "we're both tired, and we've got a big day tomorrow. Get some rest. This is tricky. We'll talk it out after the premiere."

The next evening, an hour before curtain-time, Emily was jolted from her preperformance nap. Very thin walls separated her dressing room from the boys' quarters. ". . . Goddamn you and goddamn her, too. I'm gonna fix that little bitch once and for all." There was the loud crash of a slammed door. Emily opened her own door in time to see Jerry, purple-faced with fury, grab Anya around the neck, while Rick, the stage manager, was trying to separate the lovers. It was too late. Jerry cocked his right arm, and slugged Anya with all the strength of his tall, athletic frame. Clutching her face, the girl tumbled backward over a piece of stage scenery. Even over the steady mumble of the audience filing to their seats on the other side of the curtain, Emily heard Anya's head crack the floor.

Coolly, she ignored Jerry and knelt by Anya's side. "Soak several cloths in cold water and bring them to me. Now! Rick, get Jerry out of here. Hans, you call a doctor. Tell him she may need to be hospitalized. She's unconscious, needs X rays."

After Anya was taken away in an ambulance, Emily returned to her dressing room. She sat quietly in front of the mirror, her hands toying absentmindedly with her bobby pins. Rick knocked. "What shall we do?"

"Go to the theater manager," she answered evenly. "Tell him we have to cancel. There's no way we can replace Anya half an hour before curtain-time."

"What about tomorrow? They've sold a lot of tickets—"

"I don't want to discuss it. Cancel the performances. All of them!"

When Rick returned, she was zipping up her canvas travel bag.

"Where are you going?"

"New York."

"You can't just up and leave."

"I can, and I am."

"But what should we do?"

"You have the plane tickets. The tour is finished. Everybody's paid through the week. As far as I'm concerned, there is no more company." Flagging a taxi, she never looked back at the theater marquee, boldly announcing, "Dance Drama Company."

It was my fault, she reflected, as her flight sped westward across the Atlantic. The reviews called me a genius in Edinburgh. What kind of a genius doesn't plan ahead? What kind of a genius allows something like this to destroy her own dream?

I should have foreseen the risk and provided for understudies. A genius doesn't make an elementary mistake like that.

My flaw, she thought bitterly. I mothered them, kept them happy, indulged their gossip and their moods. I wanted them to love me. A good director wouldn't have allowed it all to happen in the first place; a mother would have seen it coming, soothed it, solved it. I wanted to be both, and I wasn't either.

111

In New York, the loft was empty. John was on the road. She unpacked. Costumes and props and "Dream Dances" paraphernalia went into storage. Boxes were sealed, pushed into far corners of the basement. Records and tapes, all the music of her repertory, were filed neatly away.

Then she rested.

On the second day the phone rang. It was John. "I've been trying to call you all over Europe. Nobody seemed to know where you were."

"So, I'm home. How's your show going?"

"Somebody said you canceled London."

"That's right."

"But why? What happened?"

"Nothing happened. Everything happened. Just another Emily misfire, that's all."

"What do you mean? Are you all right?"

"Physically, sure. Mentally—fair and cooler."

"What about the company? Those dancers all depend on you."

"I don't give a damn about the company. I don't want anybody to depend on me ever again. They have their return tickets. Rick will bring them. I simply don't care."

When John returned home, he found the house tidy, closets arranged, refrigerator full. There were no dance leotards dropped hastily in corners, no dance slippers on chairs, no records spread out on the floor, no half-written scripts strewn across the typewriter. His wife was lying in bed, reading a paperback novel. Gone was the energy of creativity, the drive to work past the point of exhaustion, the stimulation of late-night discussions about art and new ideas. Bland, passive, she had simply accepted the London incident, the disbanding of her company, as final.

"Darling, you've got to snap out of this."

"Why? That phase of my life is over. Maybe this is the time to start a family."

During the months which followed, they worked together as excitedly, as thoroughly, as on any play, any choreography, to convert their loft and their lives so that they would be prepared for the baby.

Through eight-and-a-half months of pregnancy, Emily

112

continued to take a daily barre, maintaining her coordination, balance, and general body strengths despite her expansion in girth.

It was a time of joy and hopeful expectation. John's career was blossoming and their financial problems were solved. For the first time they furnished and redecorated, bought newlyweds' presents for themselves—household appliances, kitchen equipment, the pots and pans and silverware and dishes of a normal American family.

Like any loving husband and wife, they discussed the new situation, anticipated the adjustments, felt they were prepared for any problems. But there was no way to anticipate what happened when the baby was born, and afterward.

There were complications. A Caesarean delivery was necessary. But Emily insisted on remaining awake and watching the procedure. A boy. She saw him for less than two minutes.

The doctor entered her room. "Your son has a serious birth defect. If there is to be any hope of saving him, we must move him to St. Vincent's for surgery. I'll need your signature on this surgical permission form. Immediately."

Terrible hours followed—the infant's lung collapsing during the operation, his heart stopping for five minutes, conferences with doctors who predicted brain damage or death within a few weeks. A dreadful nightmare for the husband and wife who, pained and embittered, tried to console each other with intellectual discussions of the possibilities and probabilities. Five days of terrible sorrowing while they prepared and prayed for an easy death for their child whom she had seen only once.

On the evening of the fifth day, when the doctor removed her stitches, Emily asked for a large Ace bandage. "I want to start learning to walk again as soon as possible. If I can strap myself tight, maybe I can try a step or two. Maybe even tonight."

The doctor was pleased with her eagerness. "Well, I wouldn't be in quite such a hurry if I were you. But I'll order an Ace bandage. No harm in having it ready. But don't try anything without checking with the head nurse first."

"Of course," she answered brightly.

Late that night when the halls had quieted, Emily strapped her stomach tightly, struggled into her clothes, and discharged herself from the hospital. Bent in pain, she walked alone the five blocks to St. Vincent's. The sight of her baby was much as John had described. She noted his eyes—huge, blue, brightly intelligent. He seemed very much alive.

"Good-bye, David," she whispered through the glass observation wall. "I love you."

9.

Coming Apart

David came home from the hospital one month after he'd been born.

No brain damage, the doctors said. But throughout his first four years, there would be major operations and constant, difficult home care. Perhaps a private nurse should be engaged? No, Emily decided. This is my job now, to nurture this young life, to make his body as strong and beautiful as his blue eyes.

A year went by, and not quickly. Emily worked long hours each day. In addition to the usual time-consuming routine of a newborn infant, there were the surgical incisions to dress, prevention of infection, medications. She devised ingenious bindings to ease his discomfort from the dressings. To fill the child's restless hours on the table beneath a sunlamp, she invented pantomime stories with her fingers to hold his attention. He responded, learned to play. She crooned the songs of her own childhood, delighted in his attempts to match her sounds. She read to him, acting out the various roles. His eyes showed that he understood.

Soon he learned to talk, then read. She wrote "Mommy" and "Daddy" in red block letters, four inches high, on white cardboard. When David could distinguish between the two, she used smaller cards and longer words—"doctor," "pajamas," "light," "bicycle," "motorcycle." By the time he was eighteen months old, David had a fifty-word reading vocabulary. Next, Emily wrote stories on cards for him to read—"JoJo and the Infinite Cab Ride," "JoJo and His Tape Recorder," "JoJo and the Deserted Garbage Truck."

He was making progress medically, too. The doctors were encouraging. A normal life was not only possible, but probable. But little David was no replacement for Zephyr. She felt her depression growing. She felt herself going.

Each day she took a barre, keeping her muscles toned. But for what? she asked herself. Why do you hate yourself more with every *plié?* Why do you avoid thinking about dancing? And your old friends in the dance world? Face it, Emily Frankel, you couldn't handle it. No, I almost succeeded. "Dream Dances" was a wonderful work; they said so in Edinburgh. But my company let me down. Oh, no. *You* let *them* down.

David enjoyed music, she discovered. To soothe him while she worked, she played the symphonies of her childhood, the powerful masterworks. Where had all the dreams gone? What had happened to that girl, feet twinkling through sun and leaf shadows?

A record of Gustav Mahler's Fifth Symphony dropped onto the turntable. She listened to the funeral march, staring at what was once her studio mirror wall. The mirrors were now stuccoed in a pattern, paintings and drapes hung on the wall. Slivers of images reflected back at her. Was that age she saw in the distorted refractions? Did her waist look a little thicker? Were there lines in her face? She wasn't sure. I'm too young to be middle-aged, she thought. Or am I?

She slumped in a chair, thinking, as the somber Mahler played on. Fragments intruded—of her early choreography, of rehearsals with Mark, of her company, and the beautiful "Dream Dances." That life, it's gone now. No more dancing. I have nothing left to do.

She prepared John's dinner, set it out on the table. One place setting. "I'm not very hungry, John. Go ahead and eat. I think I'll read."

She lay, staring at the pages. I'm *not* middle-aged, she told herself. Physically, I'm just coming into my prime. But I'm sinking, falling away. . . .

But I'm alive. I have a beautiful son who needs me, a husband with a wonderful career. And a home, and music. As soon as David is out of danger, I will go back to dancing. I'll build a new repertory, commission new music.

But, she argued, I made no bookings the year I was pregnant. Even if I started making bookings now, they would have to be for a year from now. I don't know if there'll be enough strength left in my muscles. Anyway, how can I plan on a year from now? I don't know how David'll be in a year.

But you've started from scratch before. You can, you must do it again. . . .

No. I'm too tired. I can't.

Retreating from the world, she went outside only for essential household errands and David's trips to the doctors' offices. She began ignoring the telephone when it rang, except when the clock told her it was John's regular nightly call from the theater. Gradually, the phone rang less and less. One bright summer morning she drew the shades on the windows, and somehow never got around to pulling them back up. The outside world seemed intrusive. Out on the streets were busy people with important things to do.

The only light entering from the outside was through the skylight in the ceiling, under which John had built a subfloor, creating a small, unheated attic office. I'll write, she decided, and started spending time in the little office. Soon she was spending eight to ten hours at the typewriter.

"I like writing, John. You know, it's actually more rewarding than dancing in the long run. It really stretches my brain."

John approved. Perhaps writing would get her out of this strange mood she'd been in—dark rooms, house compulsively clean, long silences, unanswered telephone—and bring back her excitement, her drive. "I'd like to see what you've done."

"Okay. I've got a couple chapters. They're rough, but you can get an idea of what I'm going for."

"Leave them out on the kitchen table tonight when you go to bed. I'll read them when I get home."

But he was in the final rehearsals of a musical, working long hours. After rehearsal he would unwind with his friends in the cast, going to a Broadway hangout. When he got home at night, he was usually so tired he went straight to bed. She tried not to notice that he wasn't reading her work. As soon as his show opened, she reasoned, there would be more time and they would establish a routine.

Each morning, beside the stack of unread pages, she would prepare a list of the day's activities. She couldn't begin her day without a schedule of things to do: "1. Give David sun lamp. 2. Balance checkbook. 3. Call phone company re last month's bill. 4. Check fire extinguishers in building. 5. Call accountant for appointment. 6. Start taxes. . . ."

Emily had always run her household with efficiency, zipping through domestic routines so as to conserve energy for her dancing. Now she couldn't balance her checkbook. Her filing system didn't seem to work anymore. She would sit on the floor among files and scraps of paper, searching for a stray receipt. Tax forms, which she and the accountant had formerly completed in two days, now took two weeks because of her balance sheets. Once accurate but hastily scrawled, they were now neat, legible—and full of errors.

She seemed to have forgotten the best days to buy fresh meat, dairy products, fresh vegetables. She found herself double- and triple-checking kitchen shelves. Why couldn't she organize the simplest tasks; why did she scurry so much, accomplish so little; why was she so frightened?

John's musical was opening out of town. He phoned to remind her. "I open next week. I want you to be here."

But how could she? she wondered. What if David needed her and she wasn't there? All day she mustered arguments against going.

"Darling, David will be okay for overnight," John answered her arguments. "Get a baby-sitter, give her the phone number of my hotel. I need you at the opening. You know I trust your eye and your reactions, more than anyone else's, even the director's. Please be there."

118

But she didn't know what to wear.

"Wear something wild. You know how people's eyes always follow you when you enter a restaurant or a theater. Wear something crazy and wonderful."

"Well—all right, I'll try."

But on the day of the opening, she stood in the bedroom among a litter of clothes. Outfit after outfit was tried on, critically reviewed in the mirror, then discarded. Damn it, she thought, I'll just take any old thing. She grabbed a dress at random and put it on. It just wasn't right. Maybe if I fix my hair first, I'll be able to pick out an outfit.

She was due to catch the train at 5 P.M. At 2, she washed her hair and began to arrange it. She tried pigtails—not the stiff loops of childhood, but curling luxuriantly down her back. Too informal, she decided. She pulled her long hair into a topknot—too severe. She swept her hair into a stylish chignon—too chic. She tried it loose and straight, falling softly to her waist. "I look like a hippie," she muttered. It refused to curl under at her shoulders. Emily Frankel, who could change her hair between ballets in ninety seconds, who had practiced hairstyling for many hours, now found herself incapable. As five o'clock approached, she rewashed and redried, tried setting gel and curlers. Nothing worked.

Emily met the baby-sitter at the door. "I'm sorry," she said. "I should have called. I won't be needing you tonight. There's some important work I have to do here."

Except for her sleeping son, she was alone in the house. There was nothing at all to do. She paced the rooms. She had failed in every aspect of her life—she was even failing as a wife, unable to be at her husband's side when he wanted her.

The phone rang—probably John wondering where she was. She lay on her bed in the dark, not answering, despairing. In a few moments it rang again. Finally, angry, she picked it up.

It was an old trusted friend from the dance world. She hadn't heard from him in months. Or was it years? He was cheery, inquisitive. She tried to be civil, to give an explanation for her long silence. She was trying to hide her depression, but then she couldn't seem to think straight. Suddenly she burst into tears.

"Emily! What's wrong? For God's sake, what's the matter?"

She tried to answer but she just kept crying.

119

"Listen," he insisted. "I don't know what's wrong, and you don't have to tell me. But you need help. There's a friend I know, a psychiatrist. He helped me a lot. Take down his name and number. You've got to talk to somebody."

A direct command. She didn't have to decide anything. Obediently, she wrote down the doctor's name and number.

"Well, I suppose what I really want to talk about is . . ." Weeks of intensive therapy hadn't made it any easier to say. Then, in a rush: "What I want to talk about is suicide." She paused a moment. "Mine."

George said nothing. He merely nodded, and made a note on his pad.

"You see, I don't know where I got the idea, but when I was a little girl, I had this vision of how I wanted my body to look when I died. I actually played it out—I staged my own funeral. It was beautifully melancholy.

"I took some of mama's white ten-inch candles, set them up in an oval on the floor, and lit them. I had on this beautiful long white dress trimmed in lace, puffed sleeves with satin ribbons. Then I played the record of my favorite Brahms symphony. Then I lay down in the middle of the candles, folded my hands on my chest, and closed my eyes. My hair was combed in soft waves. I remember thinking how perfect I must look, thinking how sad everybody would be. They'd all be sorry, too. . . ." A slight chuckle: "That picture is still there, in my head.

"It was a death game, wasn't it?" George didn't answer. "Well," she continued, "that scene keeps playing over and over in my mind. I'm obsessed with it, George. It has something to do with the death of the dancer, doesn't it? My dancer dream."

George rarely said much. A skilled professional, he simply listened while she talked, his silence forcing her to answer her own questions. He never criticized or punished; he simply understood. She had told him everything—her pressured childhood, the failures of her adult existence and her father's predictions of failure, her fears and concerns in her marriage. Emily had absorbed a lot of psychiatric terminology and she tested him, challenged him, even

120

tried to trap him with her verbal skills. "I'm a compulsive neurotic, aren't I?"

"Well, do you think you are?" he asked.

By such steadfast refusal to supply answers, he remained consistent—and to be trusted. When she finally admitted she had made a suicide list, picked a date and a method, George expressed no disapproval.

But she began listening to music again with some of the joy and wonder of her childhood. Zephyr was gone, perhaps replaced by pleasure in the music itself. When she found herself knitting a sweater for the coming winter—planning ahead—she knew she was out of danger.

One evening she realized she had finished a sleeve several minutes before and had been simply sitting, concentrating on the music of Mahler's Fifth Symphony. What a long symphony, she thought. It goes on and on and still sustains the theme. Intrigued, she put aside her knitting and sat down to listen to the symphony again. She timed it, discovering that it held her interest for the entire seventy minutes.

At first, it seemed as if there were two themes in opposition—the inevitability of death, a tragic view; and the affirmation of life, a triumphant view. In the fourth movement she discovered peaceful acceptance. And, in the fifth, the joyous Finale Allegro, the link between the two themes—the statement that life and death coexist, black and white, joy and despair, each giving meaning and affirmation to the other.

An image crept into Emily's mind: huge orchestra, musicians fingering silver and gold instruments, starry twinkle of little lights on the music stands; in the center the godlike conductor on his podium, leading. And in a strong shaft of white light, the tiny figure of a dancer, moving with grace and power before the black-clad musicians, expressing the highs and lows, the dynamics and essence of the Mahler. The great sound of that orchestra, leading her, following her, impelling and compelling.

She laughed out loud. But dance an entire seventy-minute symphony? That's impossible. No dancer, she knew, ever attempted to sustain more than twenty solo minutes.

Perhaps, but hadn't she always attacked the impossible? Her mind was working again. Though onstage for that entire seventy minutes, a dancer could dance only the parts that lend themselves to choreography, simply sitting or kneeling and listening as part of the audience during the parts that lacked dance rhythms. And even the moments of stillness would be part of her statement.

She caught herself. *Her* statement. She still had something to say, something to communicate in dance. Impossible? Hadn't she earned the highest grades as a child? Coped with New York as a teen-ager? Learned to dance on feet so ill suited to the discipline that the doctors had advised her to quit? Formed a company and brought dance to a thousand American towns? George encouraged her idea, supported her, and gave her permission to try.

The music became a focus. She tried to attack the symphony, find boring spots or places of inconsistency, but she couldn't—it held together. Ideas for movement came in each of the five sections. Even the third, the Scherzo, which at first had seemed devoid of choreographic potential, was rich with images. Dance the entire seventy minutes? All right, permission granted. If the dancer dream was dead, why be bound by conventional thinking?

There were other questions. Would one small dancer, on stage with an orchestra of 100 to 120 musicians, detract from the music? And how much of the stage would she need, so that she would have room to dance without packing the orchestra too tightly into the area upstage of the apron? What about the conductor? She couldn't vie with him, cover him or dance directly in front of him. She should utilize his importance, his leadership, let him control her actions, too. She would have to come up with new spatial concepts. Circular movement would not work as well as the more physically demanding diagonals—block-long sprints.

There were the positive aspects, too; the orchestra, all black and white, with Emily the color—counterpoint to the musicians' strict formality. An orchestra is static, players confined to their chairs; while she had the freedom of movement.

Telling no one, she began, made notes. Her daily barre was no longer a punishing ordeal to be completed as quickly as possible; but simply a warm-up, a means to an end.

She telephoned Norman Walker, a major choreographer, a friend. "Norman, I've got this fantastic concept. I don't really know if I can do it, but I'm going to try."

122

"Interesting." Norman didn't bring up all the reasons why she couldn't do it. The only question he asked was, "Where are you in the work right now?"

"That's why I'm calling. I want you to listen to the symphony with me and see what I've done so far. Choreograph it with me."

They were a strange pair. Emily so tiny and delicate, almost fragile. Norman, a tall man with the grace and strength of a highly trained dancer. Two powerful intelligences willing to dare and be different. Walker's movement was based on Graham technique, Emily's more on classical ballet. They were a good team. In the studio—she had removed the drapes and paintings, scraped the stucco off the mirrors—he demanded, demonstrated, cajoled, then sat with her and analyzed. Often they spent an entire day working on one 2-minute segment, Walker showing her what he wanted, then driving her until she was exhausted, but had it right.

Norman wanted oversized costumes, grand cloaks, enormous props that tripled her size on stage, suiting the gigantic effect of the music and his choreography. A designer was hired to execute their ideas.

When Emily telephoned her agent, Ron, to explain the Mahler project, he brought up all the objections: "It would be impossible to get a booking, Emily. Nobody would accept it."

"This is my own concept, Ron," she argued. "It's innovative. I've got to do it." And she would, with or without his help. Finally they reached a compromise. He would watch a rehearsal before making a decision.

For the first time in three years she really danced, treating the rehearsal like a bravura performance. After seventy minutes, Ron leaned against the wall. "Emily, it's incredible. It's the most moving statement in dance I've ever seen. It won't be easy to get you a booking, but I'll start trying."

In a month he called back. Maestro Thomas Schiff, he told her, was conducting the City Symphony Society in a Mahler season at Lincoln Center in February. An innovator, Schiff was intrigued with

123

the idea of dancing to Mahler's Fifth. Such an unconventional performance would be an effective change of pace in the six-concert series.

In a few days, Ron called again. "Emily, I've got you a tryout. This is your chance to open the Mahler on the road, with a live audience, a week before bringing it in to Lincoln Center. An old friend of mine is head of the Convocations Series at Purdue University. They just had an artist cancel, and he was delighted to get you. Said he'd read about you dancing at Purdue before. They've got a beautifully equipped theater. And the best news of all, I've negotiated a five-thousand-dollar fee."

"Ron! I've never made that much before."

"Prices have gone up since—while you've been on vacation. An artist booked into Lincoln Center with the City Symphony commands high fees. What with the performance, as well as the rehearsals, you'll earn it, Emily. Of course, you'll also have the public relations duties for the university. A couple television interviews, a radio show. But I know you've never minded promoting cultural activities in the schools."

"It's like old times, isn't it, Ron?"

"Yes, dear. It's good to have you back and working again."

Finally, there was nothing left to do but pack before leaving for the airport. There was no indecision, no confusion, over selecting her wardrobe. Back in dance harness, the routine was as comfortable as her traveling uniform of blue corduroy pants, blue jersey shirt, and the old black boots with square toes that eased the pressure on her toes. For television appearances, she decided that the short, clinging lavender jersey dress, gray heels, and gray stockings would be appropriate. The beautiful string of antique amber beads would go well with the outfit.

John watched her drop them into the white carryall bag. "Do you really think you should take that?" he asked as she took out her favorite coat, the chic gray Lord & Taylor with its antique silver jewel. "Might be a little fancy for Purdue."

"John, I want to look fancy. Anyway, it's cold in Indiana this time of year."

At the airport, heads turned as this exotic woman with small, pale face and striking clothes walked the concourse. "Hey!" she grinned at John. "Zephyr's about to fly."

With her plane off the runway and soaring into the sky, John bought a newspaper for the taxi ride home. The weather report for Indiana wasn't good, he noticed. They were predicting snow. I hope she gets a good, safe driver out there, he thought. But it was a small worry, quickly dismissed. After all, his Emily was on the brink of a new direction in her work. Whatever had been bothering her was resolved for now. He couldn't wait to see her again.

10.

Indianapolis Hospital

The sign plainly read "No Smoking." Just as plainly, John sat beneath it, lighting a new cigarette from the butt of his old one. A surgical nurse passed by and frowned at him. He ignored her, keeping his eyes on the double doors through which Dr. Sam or Dr. Morrison would eventually appear.

Six and a half hours after they had wheeled Emily into the operating room, the two doctors walked out. Dr. Morrison turned on his heel and strode off up the hallway, while his Oriental colleague approached. He was glad to report that the operation, though long and difficult, had gone well. There had been no unexpected complications. The only serious problem had been an excessive formation of callus—a development they had anticipated.

"And I do have some good news. When we exposed the nerve tissue in her spine, we applied electrodes to certain ganglia. We tested her neural response below the waist and were able to produce a full range of movement on her right side and about eighty-five percent on her left side."

127

"In other words, she's normal, or nearly normal? That she'll be able—"

"To walk again? Yes, I think so. Given a normal recovery without complications."

"And dancing?"

"Well, John, that is much harder to determine. But given your wife's extraordinary tenacity and determination, I would say that her chances of performing again are excellent. How long? In many ways, that's up to her. She could be back on her feet in a year to eighteen months. From there, how long it takes her to get back into shape is something none of us can predict."

"But Dr. Morrison told her—"

"I know what Dr. Morrison told your wife. I heard about it this morning, and that she was very distressed. All I can tell you is that Dr. Morrison is very conservative. He believes in expecting the worst, and then being pleasantly surprised if something better happens. Also, he doesn't know your wife like I do. I believe that emotional factors can modify or alter what mathematics and pure science tell us."

"Damn, I hope so. Thanks a lot, Dr. Sam, for everything, for more than you know."

The doctor nodded pleasantly. "One more thing. As a post-op patient, Emily won't need to be in Intensive Care anymore. I've assigned her a private room on the surgical wing. That ought to please her. You can meet her back in her room in, oh, say five hours, after she's back from Recovery. You might want to get there a little ahead of time. The nurses have received a lot of flowers and letters and gifts, and they're running out of space. You might want to figure out some kind of arrangement."

Her awareness had ceased shortly after the anesthetist had plunged his needle into her arm. She had begun the count backward from 100, and the black cone had swept in cutting off sight of surgeons and nurses and operating room, spinning her quickly down the sides of the whirlpool. At the bottom she had been encased in cotton, relieved of the burden of control. There was a gap; something important had happened. Now, much against her will, she was spinning back up toward the light. She must begin to think again.

128

Oh yes—the back operation. Now she remembered. She had no way of determining how much time had gone by, but she was fairly certain that the long-awaited operation was over. I suppose I'm in the recovery room now.

She opened her eyes, glanced from side to side. Sheet-covered patients on railed stretchers surrounded her. Many bore evidence of major surgery—the bulge of wrappings disguising the locations where major organs had once functioned, had failed, had been removed. She heard the buzzes and clicks of life-support equipment, punctuated by occasional groans. Muted voices called urgent messages over the intercom. White-skirted nurses bustled from patient to patient.

At the movement of Emily's head, one of the white clad figures moved to her side. "Hello there. How are we feeling this afternoon?"

"I don't really know yet." Emily said. "I can't seem to feel much of anything."

"Of course. You've been under some pretty heavy anesthesia. It'll be wearing off soon."

"I'd like some water, please."

"Oh, I'm afraid that isn't allowed. Too soon after your operation."

"How did it go?"

"Your doctor will report to you after you go back upstairs."

"Well, what about when the anesthetic wears off. Will I feel pain?"

"Perhaps a little discomfort, but that's all."

The nurse hurried off as another patient regained consciousness. Emily relaxed on her pallet, awaiting the onset of postoperative pain that she was sure would come.

In fact, she *wanted* to feel pain, rather than the present vague, not-quite-there fuzziness she felt in her body. Pain was an old familiar adversary with whom she had learned to deal.

She lifted a tentative hand and wiggled her fingers slightly. At least she still retained the use of her upper body.

She used her newfound hand to reach below her waist. Her fingers told her she was touching her legs; but as far as the skin of her thighs was concerned, she might as well have been touching the mattress. Withdrawing her hand, she felt something hard and slick to

129

the touch. Tracing it, she realized that she was still in restraints—the strap across her pelvis bound her tightly to the bed. A second strap was in its accustomed place, across her lower rib cage.

Then nothing's changed, Emily told herself. There's no feeling in my legs; I'm probably strapped to a Stryker bed. The operation failed.

She waited for an hour, as recorded on the electric wall clock. Nurses came and went, monitoring her supply of intravenous fluid. She waited, mentally searching for pain in her legs. Any feeling at all would mean that her legs would work again, walk again.

No, she cautioned herself, don't get caught in that trap. Dr. Morrison said it would take five years *if* the operation was a success. And it's beginning to look like the surgery didn't work. Emily, you should know by now, miracles happen only to other people.

She thought of people she knew, or had seen, in wheelchairs. They seemed to adjust, hold jobs, entertain themselves. If they could, well then, so could she.

She decided not to think about wheelchairs any more; it was destructive. George had explained that reality was the way in which her mind perceived a situation. John had told her she must use her ability as an artist to think positively. Well, then, I suppose I must get on with my life. The back operation was just one more possibility that didn't work out.

It was a relief, in a way. Mentally she lay back and rested, free from the compulsion to drive herself. No more exhaustion; no more hunger—there was a thought! Now she could eat what she wanted, when she wanted; forget the bathroom scale as one forgets a childhood enemy.

Being confined to a wheelchair wouldn't prevent me from writing, Emily thought. It would be a lot of work, but fun and challenging. A world as difficult to conquer as dancing, maybe even more difficult. There was a thick file in her desk at home, full of notes and odd scraps of paper on which she had jotted ideas for stories through the years. When she returned home, she would see if any of the ideas still appealed to her.

The recovery room nurses came and went, checking her blood pressure and pulse rate. When she had first come out of the anesthesia, both had been dangerously low. By the time the nurses finally discharged her, almost all the other post-op patients had been wheeled away. Attendants—unfamiliar faces because it was a different shift now—appeared, ready to wheel her away. She watched the hallway's fluorescent light fixtures flick by overhead, felt the accustomed lurch of the elevator. Nothing's changed, she thought. Everything's the same as it was this morning. A wasted day.

On her floor, she realized that the attendants were turning the wrong way, away from the Intensive Care ward. "Where are you taking me?" she asked.

"To your room."

They braked in front of a door, pushed it open. "Sir," one attendant spoke to John, "would you mind waiting out in the hall for a moment? While we get your wife off the cart and into her bed?"

John peered at her face as he stepped out of the room, slipping past her cart. "How do you feel, honey?" he asked.

"Have I really got a room now, a real room of my own?"

There was no time for him to answer as she was whisked inside. She looked eagerly about her as the attendants aligned the stretcher and bed. The room was so bright it hurt her eyes to look. Not her cubicle in Intensive Care but a real room, with a window and furniture and most of all, privacy. She closed her eyes as they lifted her to the Stryker bed.

Not until the attendants had gone and John had reentered did she dare open her eyes again. Her first impression had been right—there were flowers, boldly colorful blooms, everywhere. Huge chrysanthemums filled corners with their brilliant hues. Daisies peeked through the long stems of roses, their regal red and yellow petals stretching toward the ceiling. Delicate lilies of the valley vied for her attention with pure white blooms of Easter lilies. Makeshift vases had been brought in, but still there weren't enough. Bunches of flowers were simply stacked or leaned against the wall.

The smells, the fragrant aromas, had driven the hospital odors to full retreat. Despite the dirty, black, budless branches outside her window, where winter retained its grip on the bleak Indiana plain, spring had come to her room. No matter what she had decided during the long hours in Recovery, she felt reborn.

"All these flowers. They're so beautiful. How . . .? Who . . .?"

"They're from all your friends, all the people who love

131

you. People back home, dancers, actors, producers, the dance students at Purdue, your mother—and me, too." She placed her hand over her eyes, covering the tears she sensed welling close to the surface.

"And there are more," John went on, "in the mailroom here at the hospital. We can't figure out where to put them all."

"Oh, bring them in. Stack them on top of each other. Cover the floor with them. I want to see them all."

"And we don't even have enough room for all the cards and telegrams and letters." John pushed a stack of mail across her bed table. The pile almost toppled. At random, she selected a telegram and tore it open. It was from her agent.

EMILY. YOU ARE READY FOR REAL COMEBACK STOP HAVE BOOKED YOU WITH NY CITY SYMPHONY SOCIETY FOR NEXT YEAR STOP HAVE FEELERS FROM SOUTH AMERICA STOP SHALL WE BOOK TOUR? LOVE RON.

A booking! A tour! A skinny little girl, lying paralyzed in her Stryker bed, and Maestro Thomas Schiff's great orchestra wanted her to dance for them! It was almost too much. Her room was in bloom and her life was beginning to bloom again. She cried.

Through her tears she saw that the *Time* magazine was at the bottom of the pile of letters. She remembered the *penché* picture, envisioned herself centered, balanced, arched high, extended gracefully, leaning so gracefully toward the floor, a perfect swan.

She would put herself back in and start all over. She would wind up her mainspring and try again.

She *would* move her feet. . . .

11.
Walking

Dr. Morrison entered Emily's room trailed by four attendants carrying a huge basin, stirring paddles, and armloads of boxes. "Are you my tailors?" she asked. "Here to create a chic plaster gown?"

Morrison and Sam seemed satisfied that the operation had been a success. One week in the Stryker bed, sufficient time for the fusion to begin strengthening, and she was ready for the next step, her plaster cast.

Dr. Morrison rolled up his sleeves and went to work. First they flipped her Stryker bed into the face-down position. With Morrison observing, it was a much gentler maneuver than usual. Then they dumped several boxes of powder into the basin, followed by water, and began stirring vigorously. While the plaster was hardening into the proper consistency, they applied a layer of gauze to Emily's exposed back. Finally, Dr. Morrison dipped his hands into the basin, drew out a double handful, and spread it over the gauze, shaping it to her contours.

133

"That stuff is cold," she shuddered. "It feels funny.'"

"Well, that's to be expected," Dr. Morrison said. "It won't feel so bad once it dries. You're going to get accustomed to the cast just as if it were your own skin. We have to make it as tight as possible so you'll be able to move on your own, while preventing any movement whatsoever in your back."

After they completed a layer, another gauze sheet was trimmed and fitted, followed by another layer of plaster, and another, until they had molded five layers in all. Then the crew left. Morrison promised to return when the plaster on her back had dried sufficiently. It was a strange feeling, lying face down on the Stryker bed, with an unaccustomed, uncomfortable weight on her back. But Emily was content. She had reached another plateau.

In two hours, Morrison returned with a new team of attendants and tapped the cast with his fingernail. Deciding that it had hardened sufficiently, they flipped the bed even more cautiously than before, so that Emily was lying face up.

Now she could watch the procedure. Here, she thought in wonder, is a skilled surgeon, with fingers capable of delicate surgery on bones and nerve tissue, up to his elbows in plaster. "It must stick to your fingers, get under your fingernails. How do you ever get it off?"

"Simple," he answered. "I'm wearing disposable rubber gloves. So when I'm finished, I just take off the gloves and throw them away."

Like a sculptor, Morrison gently shaped the plaster to her body. The cast, she now realized, would extend from her neck to her upper thighs. She giggled in embarrassment as he molded the gauze across her chest. "Hey, can I order a new shape while you're at it?"

He laughed with her. "I'm no Michaelangelo, you know."

After completing the front of the cast, they worked down her sides, smoothing a seam between the front and back portions. After a full morning's work, they gathered up their tools and left her to dry. "Try not to move for four hours," Morrison cautioned her. "Think of it this way: These are the last four hours you'll have to concentrate on immobility. Just a little while longer, and you can relax for the first time since you came in here."

So she lay, amid the plaster debris and the soggy sheets, once again concentrating on the passage of time. Three hours to go, then two. As her skin alerted her that the cast was indeed hardening,

134

she realized that the Stryker bed and its straps would only be replaced by a new discomfort. She understood what a turtle must feel like—body encased in a hard shell, head, arms, and legs sticking out. And a turtle lying on its back is helpless. I'm going to learn to turn myself over.

Late in the afternoon, attendants gently transferred her from the Stryker bed to a real hospital bed. "Can I try to move around by myself?" she asked. "If I get tired lying on my back, can I try to turn over?"

"Certainly." How could Dr. Morrison explain the near-impossibility of such a task to this willful woman? She had as yet produced no movement below her waist, though he felt the nerve tissue was beginning to respond. Her arm and shoulder muscles had been unused for over six weeks. "You can try, but don't expect much success. Ask the nurses for help when you want to turn over."

To Emily, "help" meant a tool with which she would help herself. "Could I have a bar attached over my head, so I could hold it and practice pull-ups? Strengthen my arms and shoulders?"

"If you feel you want to try pulling yourself up like that, I can have a grab bar installed. But don't overdo it. The head of our Physical Therapy Department, Mrs. Morgan, will be in to see you tomorrow, discuss your therapy program with you, and tell you just what to expect in the way of progress. She knows just how much how soon you can do."

"That's wonderful, Doctor." As he left the room, she called after him, "Would you have the grab bar installed this evening, please?"

Well, Em, here you go again. Back to work. How was it that tortoise won the race against the hare? By sticking with it, keeping going, never quitting. That's what I am, another turtle. Slow and steady wins the race. I don't give up. Here I am with the chance to choose again. And again I choose to dance.

The first time around, she knew, she had chosen dancing for child's reasons—Daddy's music, Zephyr, and her sisters—Sara's choice of writing, Debra's of acting; and the necessity to have her own unique form of expression. This time, she told herself, you've got adult reasons. It's my craft, my language, and it's something I'm good at. And I'm not finished. I almost succeeded before; this time I'll try harder.

If Morrison says five years, I'll try to make it four. If four,

135

then I'll go for three, or two, or one. That's my turtle talk. I may be a turtle now, but wait till I get out of this shell. I'll learn to step, to stand, to walk, to run, and ride my bike and climb and *relevé* and jump and *penché arabesque.* I will! Better than ever.

As soon as her evening meal was over, when the nurses and attendants left her alone with the newly-installed grab bar, she reached with her right hand and carefully gripped the steel rod. Now, lift! she told her arm muscles. But nothing happened. She tried again, narrowing the focus of her will to the muscles of her forearm, blanking everything else from her mind. Was there movement? She thought she detected a half-inch separation between her back and the sheet, but she wasn't sure. Sweating with the effort, she pulled harder.

Her weight, she calculated, was down from her usual 110 to perhaps 92 pounds. The cast weighed 15. Dancing, she had performed lifts, requiring momentary bursts of incredible strength. At home, she had put her shoulder behind a piano in her studio and moved it on rollers; she had dragged loudspeakers up the four flights to her loft. But nothing had ever seemed as difficult as this. She worked with her right arm, then her left, uncertain of any results.

Leverage, she thought, that's the answer. This turtle is going to flip herself over. She found that if she pulled on the bed's side rail with her left hand, and at the same time lifted with her right on the grab bar, her body would begin to roll up onto her left shoulder. But she always toppled back. Again she tried. And again. "Come on, Emily," she gritted. "Now. Pull. Push." She flung her head to the left and flopped gracelessly over onto her face.

Unable to reverse the maneuver, she buzzed the night nurse. "I seem to have gotten myself in a bit of a bind. Help me roll over onto my back."

The following morning, Emily was trying to duplicate her roll-over when a voice interrupted her. "Whoa. Take it easy. Save some of that energy for me." Emily glanced toward the door. The voice belonged to a tiny woman, smaller than Emily.

"Miss Frankel? I'm Mrs. Morgan, your physical

therapist." She appeared wiry, rather than muscular, of an indeterminate age. Unheeded wisps of gray hair poked from beneath her starched white cap. Rimless bifocals slid down her nose away from bird-bright eyes. "I'm sure you expected a burly, blond Swedish masseuse type. But I assure you I'm quite strong. Other patients of mine have said I can be as tough as a Notre Dame linebacker—since I've been here, in fact, I've had quite a few of the football boys under my care. I mention them specifically because I understand you're a professional dancer. So I'm starting with the assumption that you are as strong and physically coordinated as any athlete."

"Well, I used to be, anyway."

"Perhaps you will be again—if you're as hard a worker as Dr. Sam says."

"I've worked hard all my life," Emily said. "I don't see any reason to stop now."

"Good. Tomorrow morning you'll be brought to the Physical Therapy Department."

"What do I do first?"

"We start you out on the tilt table. You've been lying down more than six weeks, so we have to accustom your body to being vertical. The table is something like a Stryker bed, though not nearly as painful. We proceed gradually, increasing the angle daily, and increasing the amount of time on the table."

"But is that all, Mrs. Morgan? Just the tilt table? Don't you do anything else?"

"Not right away. Before you can do anything else, you must learn to be in the upright position again."

"But don't you do any manipulation of my muscles or limbs? That *is* part of the physical therapy program, isn't it?"

"Of course. But that comes later, after the tilt table. I will exercise your muscles for you, manipulate them to restore the blood circulation and muscle tone. And gradually, as your brain relearns the signals, you'll take over and manipulate them yourself."

"Couldn't you start that process now? This morning? Here in my bed?"

"I have another patient waiting for me upstairs. And besides, you're not ready yet. I told you, you have to master the tilt table first. Don't be in such a hurry."

"Mrs. Morgan, I want to be home with my son and husband. John is already getting some names of good physical

137

therapists in New York who'll be able to continue the work you and I begin here."

"That's fine. But let's not think so far ahead. You and I have a great deal of work to do before we can begin talking about going home."

"How long, Mrs. Morgan? How long?"

"I'm sorry, I can't answer that yet. I'll know better in a few weeks, after I've seen how hard you're willing to work."

The trip to Physical Therapy was an ordeal. The attendants were deliberate, in no haste lest they endanger her still-fragile spine. It took the better part of fifteen minutes to shift Emily to the rolling stretcher, ride down the hallway and up the elevator under the collective gaze of the curious, then down another long hallway to a separate wing and through the double doors of the therapy room.

"Okay," Emily exclaimed brightly when Mrs. Morgan approached, "where's this awful tilt table? I'm ready."

She was lifted to the table and strapped down. An attendant turned the elevating crank, raising her fifteen degrees above horizontal. From this vantage point, she surveyed her new surroundings.

The room was stark white, bright sunlight from the windows contrasting with the room's occupants. Patients of all ages and sizes were working under, over, and on a maze of equipment that seemed to belong in an expensive health club. On a mat lay a young boy—immobile, yet with the red face and pouring sweat of intense effort. An elderly man struggled to master prosthetic legs. A woman sat sobbing and unattended in a whirlpool. A young man, with the muscular upper body and rugged build of an athlete, tottered on a plaster-encased leg, clinging to parallel bars.

Emily began to feel lightheaded. But I'm going to take it, she told herself. And when Mrs. Morgan comes back to let me down, I'm going to ask her to leave me a little longer. Then she began to feel nausea.

138

"Mrs. Morgan," she called against the general hubbub in the room. "Mrs. Morgan. I'm afraid I'm going to be sick."

The little therapist hurried over. "That's perfectly normal, Miss Frankel. Everybody feels sick to their stomach the first time. But try and make it two more minutes. I'd like you to do five minutes today."

Emily fought the urge to vomit as she watched Mrs. Morgan's retreating back. Suddenly whirling pools of black appeared before her eyes. She blinked rapidly, but the sensation only intensified. She imagined she was pitching forward and gratefully gave herself up to the sense of falling.

The next thing she knew, she was lying flat, the tilt table again horizontal, Mrs. Morgan bending over her.

"What happened?"

"It appears that you fainted. I think you've done enough for the first day."

"Please! You said two more minutes. I have to get used to it. Please let me try it again."

"I don't think that's advisable. Tomorrow we'll see if you can go the full five minutes, and then try to work up to ten. Then we can tilt the table higher. I'll call for the attendants to take you back now."

The tilt table continued to be an insurmountable obstacle to further progress. Always the discomfort, followed by the nausea, and then the dizziness. Determination was not enough. And Mrs. Morgan was adamant: Until Emily could endure a fully vertical position for thirty minutes, she could not go on.

"I understand how frustrating it is for you, my dear. But your doctors have laid out this program for you, and I can't go against their orders. Try not to be discouraged—the first day you couldn't even do five minutes. Now you're almost up to fifteen."

"But have other patients of yours taken this long?"

"All patients are different—their injuries are different, their healing time is different." Before Emily could break in, she

139

continued, "But early in each patient's therapy, we don't have enough information to tailor a specific program. So we start with what has proved generally effective in the past—in your case, the tilt table—and change the program later if indicated."

Emily argued, "Well, I've been on this tilt table a week. Maybe I don't need to be vertical to start re-learning how to use my feet. Would you at least consider manipulating my feet while I'm on the table?"

Mrs. Morgan agreed to try. Each day, as Emily struggled with vertigo, the therapist worked with her patient's feet—massaging, bending, rotating. Then the arches. Then the ankles. Concentration on the new procedure helped Emily fight the nausea.

"I feel your touch on my skin," Emily said. "Why can't I feel the sense of movement?"

Mrs. Morgan explained, "The body's nervous system is like an electrical circuit. When the mind decides on a specific movement, it flashes a signal out along the wires, the nerve tissue. The nerves for the lower body are all concentraterd in the spine before branching out.

"When your back was broken, the communication between your brain and legs was interrupted. While you were on your back, immobile, for six weeks, the nerve tissue 'forgot' how to function, both because of disuse, and lack of blood circulation.

"That's where the tilt table comes in. Your increasing vertical position aids blood circulation to your legs. That's why you can begin to feel touch; you *are* making progress on the table. The nerve tissue is returning to life. The sensory nerves near the surface are the simplest and easiest. The nerves that signal movement, motor response, are deeper and take longer. But they'll come back, too, as we keep working."

Emily interrupted, "You mean because my brain 'forgot' how to send those electrical signals during the six weeks, you're reversing the process now."

"Yes," Mrs. Morgan answered. "By manipulation of your feet, and as the nerve tissue is rehabilitated, your brain will gradually 'remember' how the motor signals feel."

Emily asked, "Is it possible to control the signals the brain sends out in order to produce a finer dance technique?"

"I work a lot with athletes, and they learn their sport by imitation—doing the movement first, then learning the brain signals.

140

I've never worked with a dancer, but I would assume that you learn by imitation, too."

"Exactly. A dancer learns from teachers who are usually ex-dancers. They are passing down techniques that have been used for hundreds of years. But it seems that if I could train my mind, I could isolate the exact muscles I needed to execute a technical feat. The movement could be more brilliant. I'd be a better dancer.

"Would you loan me some books on physical therapy? Technical books on the nervous system? I certainly have lots of time to read. It would give me a real project to work on while I'm here."

Mrs. Morgan readily agreed.

John was telling her of rehearsal problems with his current show, David's activities, neighborhood items of interest. Emily was only half listening, glaring in concentration at the toes of her right foot, imagining an electrical impulse in her brain, making it travel down her spine and past the fusion, racing down her right leg and into the foot, finally activating the big toe's flexor muscle. Suddenly, something went "click" in her mind, and the toe wiggled. In amazement, she watched the toe move, then clenched her teeth and tried to repeat the success. Again, the "click"—and the toe wiggled again.

"John, look," she interrupted him. "I can move my toe!"

She worked on, repeating her success with the big toe, clicking the other four toes into action, and even producing a slight flex in her ankle. She danced the merry little dance of her right foot until her exhausted brain finally yielded and surrendered to a deep, dreamless sleep.

The next morning, before the attendants in Physical Therapy had a chance to place her on the tilt table, she called to Mrs. Morgan. "I've learned how to work the toe flexors, and I think I've almost figured out how to activate the side of the ankle. That's the peroneus brevis muscle, isn't it?" She demonstrated her new talent, showed off her newly-learned vocabulary.

Mrs. Morgan shared the triumph. "Well then, let's concentrate on getting the inner ankle working. And maybe even the gastrocnemius."

"The calf," Emily said, proud of her new knowledge.

The day's session was twice as long as their usual time together. Excitedly they discussed tendons, ligaments, the tiny bones in the foot, and Mrs. Morgan showed her patient how to move the ankle from side to side, up and down, in small circles, using the gastrocnemius.

Emily redoubled her efforts. Writing out a list and schedule of exercises, she worked in her room, beginning each session with a review of what she had learned up to that point. Then she went to the muscles of the upper body—fingers, wrists, arms, shoulders, and torso—with stretching and twisting exercises and pull-ups on the grab bar.

Most of the work on her lower body had to be mental— practicing the signal-sending system to isolate groups of muscles, then single muscles. How to flex, rotate, point, lift, tense, relax— each muscle had to re-learn these commonplace activities.

One movement she could manage was to lift her knee without using the muscles which were encased in her turtle shell. There *were* ways; she just had to experiment until she found them. After discovering a method that worked for her right knee, she tried her left. Like a recalcitrant twin, it followed slowly along, never quite achieving the right leg's improvement.

Within the cast her body sweated and wasted. She developed an enormous appetite. When the nurse brought in the day's menu each morning, Emily would check off a lumberjack's quantity of food. Yet when the meals were brought, she would push them away half eaten. I guess my eyes are bigger than my stomach, she would rationalize. She would detect a slight nausea as she tried to swallow. I must be too excited about my work, she decided.

As the days went by, Emily began planning to walk. "Mrs. Morgan, I've accomplished a lot. Let's go on. Would you let me try standing up, with people supporting me? I could drag my feet, like trying a step."

Mrs. Morgan referred her request to Emily's doctors.

Dr. Morrison was adamantly opposed. "Walking is out of the question. And we don't know whether the slight paralysis in your left leg is temporary or permanent."

"But Dr. Morrison, I want to go home to New York and continue my therapy work there. How can I go home unless you allow me to try learning to walk?"

Mrs. Morgan took Emily's side in the doctors' discussions. "Over the past couple of weeks it has occurred to me that perhaps we shouldn't be so rigid in insisting that all patients follow practically identical programs.

"I think we have her mental state, her emotions, to consider. This woman has survived a severe medical crisis. She is so determined, so affirmative, I think she's at least partially responsible for the rapid progress she has demonstrated. I believe her case requires a recognition of the mind's contribution to healing—something that's been missing in physical therapy programs. We are dealing with someone with high intelligence and imagination. It's up to us to be flexible. If we don't allow her a sense of progress, then she may lose the will to keep working."

Dr. Morrison said, "It's purely a medical problem. She has to be able to tolerate the tilt table so she won't faint or stumble when we let her stand. Unquestionably something is responsible for her inability to tolerate the table—a circulatory problem or something in her digestive tract which we don't understand yet."

Dr. Sam interrupted, "Mrs. Morgan, do you have a specific proposal?"

"I think I can offer a compromise," she answered. "I have a good staff in Physical Therapy. They're professionals and they know what to do. I think we should allow Miss Frankel to stand supported by the attendants. They will take all of her weight and it will have the same effect as the tilt table. If she suffers the vertigo she will know it and ask to lie down."

Dr. Morrison looked at his colleague. "What do you say to that, Dr. Sam? After all, you've been in charge of her case from the beginning."

"I believe the risk is as minimal as we can provide with the assistance of Mrs. Morgan's attendants. Emily's mental state is a major factor; I've been closer to her than you have throughout the case. I recommend we let her try standing. We've flipped the coin four times and it's come up heads four times. She's on a winning streak. Let's flip it one more time."

"The odds say this time it's going to come up 'tails,'" Morrison grumbled. "But, okay, you have my permission."

143

Instead of stopping at the tilt table, the two attendants—
by now Emily called them her "drivers"—wheeled her to an exercise
mat on the floor where an unsmiling Mrs. Morgan was waiting.
"We're going to give you your chance to stand up."

Emily was jubilant, but her therapist's expression
warned her to listen carefully. "Dr. Morrison feels that this could be
dangerous for you. And I am responsible, primarily, for overriding
his objections. So do exactly as I tell you, not the slightest bit more.
All right?"

Emily nodded as Mrs. Morgan outlined each step of the
procedure. She warned that Emily would feel even more nausea and
dizziness than she had on the table, but was to stand as long as she
could. The critical point was to not try to go beyond her endurance.

The attendants raised her to a sitting position on the cart,
then turned her so that her legs dangled over the edge. Next they
lifted her upper body and gently lowered her. With their hands
under her armpits supporting her weight, she was barely aware that
the soles of her feet were flat on the floor.

Emily enjoyed the unaccustomed freedom of standing
erect. But the familiar nausea was beginning, the blackness appear-
ing at the edge of her vision. She forced her mind away from the
situation, by counting the number of windows in the huge room, the
number of light fixtures, the number of patients. But after five
minutes, she could avoid the sickness no longer. "Okay," she gritted,
"better put me . . . down." Her head started to slump forward. The
attendants gripped her even tighter and laid her gently on the mat.
After a rest period, she was ready for the familiar routine of muscle
manipulation and weight lifting.

The tilt table was forgotten. Each day's routine began
with the standing exercise. Each day she managed to remain upright
a little longer. Each day the attendants allowed her legs to support a
little more weight.

In two weeks she had managed to remain upright for
twenty minutes, longer than she'd ever achieved on the tilt table.

The goal of going home spurred her to withstand the
weakness and nausea an extra thirty seconds, an extra minute. She

144

knew that the next phase involved proving to the doctors that she could stand without the attendants' help.

"You know," she suggested to Mrs. Morgan one morning, "after all the weight lifting I've been doing, my arms are pretty strong. I'd like to try supporting myself in a standing position between the parallel bars. The attendants could stay right by in case my grip slips, but they wouldn't have to stand here supporting me. Anyway, I've been taking most of my weight on my feet lately. Can I try, please?"

The suggestion was forwarded to her doctors. Morrison said, "It's difficult for me to believe what she's accomplished so far. It appears that you were right, Mrs. Morgan; I'll admit she's been a continual surprise to me. Okay. Let her keep going—take the usual precautions."

The "usual precautions" were maintained—the attendants staying close in case she should waver. And within a very few days, Mrs. Morgan accepted the fact that Emily was strong enough to hold herself up. The attendants were excused; soon Mrs. Morgan gained enough confidence to leave Emily standing alone while she went off to her other patients.

And as Emily's strength and endurance increased, the possibility of walking on crutches no longer seemed so remote. Standing alone between the bars, she watched other patients learning to walk with crutches. She analyzed how they shuffled their feet swinging their weight to accomplish a step; how their arms on the crutch handles supported their weight. That's what she had to learn to do, and these bars were about the same height as the crutch handles.

In her room she mentally rehearsed the movements she would need to take a step. The next day, as soon as Mrs. Morgan turned away, she began.

Slowly, she slid her right foot six inches ahead, slid her right hand six inches along the bar, then stopped to consider what she had done. When she was certain she could support herself in the new position, she came to the tricky part—shifting her weight to her right leg, definitely quite weak and still somewhat unresponsive. This, she thought wryly, must be what trapeze aerialists must feel like when they let go of the swing and sail out over thin air, trusting their partners to be there to catch them.

145

Well, I've got to either do it or not do it, she thought to herself. I can't stay here like this. Before she had time to decide, "This is the moment," she swung her right shoulder forward and transferred the combined weight of her body and the cast fully onto her right leg. The knee buckled; her momentum threatened to topple her forward. But her right hand clung to the bar. Catching herself, she straightened and locked her right knee. All that was left was to drag her left foot six inches forward.

She hung on the bars then, gasping with the effort and sheer audacity of it. It had taken nearly all her reserves of strength, concentration, and willpower, but it was done! She had taken her first step since the accident nearly three months before.

When Mrs. Morgan returned to continue the day's routine, she didn't notice the six-inch advance. Emily didn't mention it. She was remembering the long-ago days when she was touring with her dance company in the van, and they would sing songs to pass the time, usually to the tune of "Farmer in the Dell." As Mrs. Morgan worked with her, she hummed to herself: One more step to go, one more step to go, I'll walk a while, I'll rest a while, one more step to go.

In succeeding days, Emily drove herself onward. After improving her technique with one step, she tried two, dragging the rear foot ahead of the front, a snail's walk.

The day she first noticed Emily's progress along the bars, Mrs. Morgan's high-pitched voice called: "What do you think you're doing?"

"I'm moving," Emily answered proudly. "But I guess you can't really call it walking yet."

"I can't believe it," Mrs. Morgan reported to Dr. Sam that evening. "She's walking."

"Who's walking?" Dr. Morrison asked, walking in on the conference.

"Emily Frankel. This morning I found her halfway along the parallel bars."

"Are you sure she didn't get there with somebody's help?"

"Positive. I left her as I always do, up at the end of the bars. The only other people in the room were patients. She did it on her own."

Dr. Sam smiled. "That little woman has confounded every theory we've had since she's been here. Now she's taught herself to walk."

"I suppose you think next week she'll be dancing," Morrison chuckled.

"I'll tell you one thing," Sam answered. "I think she'll be dancing one day, sooner than we expect. I think we had all better revise our predictions concerning this lady. There seems to be some factor operating in her case that we've not seen before."

"I'll tell you what the factor is," Mrs. Morgan interrupted. "It's called guts. I point her out to all the other therapy patients, as an example of what they can accomplish. I was so proud of her today I could have cried, but I was too shocked."

"Well," Dr. Sam announced, "When she tells us she wants to try something new, I think we'd better start paying attention. It would appear that whether we give her permission or not, our dancer lady is going to do it anyway."

"You know what she's going to ask next," Morrison retorted. "She's going to ask to be allowed to go home!"

"At this point, I think we'd better say yes. If we don't, one of these nights she might just gather up her clothes, shuffle out the door, and hail a taxi."

Morrison smiled at the picture in spite of his professional reservations. "Look, it does me good to see what determination can accomplish. I know that she's proven me wrong at every turn, but medically, I just can't let her go home. She'd have a child to take care of, a house, a husband. And who knows what she'd try when we weren't around to keep an eye on her?"

"Let me make a proposal," Sam said. "I think she should walk the length of the parallel bars. That's about ten feet, isn't it?" Mrs. Morgan nodded assent.

"And then ask her to turn around and come back to the starting point. That would more than satisfy me. Would it you, Ed?"

"I'm just so damned afraid she's going to hurt herself, after all she's been through. But yes, I suppose ten feet down the bars

147

and ten back would be enough. And the bars work much like crutches. With her intelligence, she should make that analogy."

"All right," Sam said, "then it's settled."

Back in her room, Emily was practicing. After edging herself backward off the bed, she slid crabwise around it, leaning forward into the mattress just in case.

"Oh-ho," Sam's voice boomed behind her. "So that's how you got so good at walking."

Dr. Sam, her truest friend during the long ordeal, described the test. "When you accomplish that, we'll begin processing you for release. It'll take a couple of days, and while that's going on, you can learn to use crutches."

"Shall we set the test for tomorrow morning at, say, ten-thirty, Dr. Sam? I need some time to prepare."

"Don't you think you need more time than that to prepare?" Sam asked. "We were thinking more in terms of weeks—two anyway. Let you work up to it gradually."

"No, Doctor. It's like my dancing—there's nothing like the actual experience of performing. That's when I do my best, not in rehearsal. Let me perform tomorrow—a live performance, like I was supposed to give at Purdue." She paused a moment, added, "We could sell some tickets."

When he was gone, Emily continued practicing. But now there was a new requirement: she had to learn to turn herself around. Sagging to the bed, weary from the effort, then pushing herself upright again for another attempt, she finally found a way. Planting her weaker foot, she shuffled her right foot around in a tiny semicircle, stretching out her right hand to grab the bed as she let go with her left.

It was an ungainly maneuver, but she grinned in delight. "After all," she told her empty room, "they didn't say I had to pirouette!"

148

The next morning, she bantered cheerfully as the attendants began the long, difficult transfer to the Physical Therapy department. "This is my last round-trip ticket for this ride. Next time you guys drive me anyplace, it'll be down to the front door. I'm going home."

As if for a performance, she had prepared herself. She was wearing a ruffled nightdress, a gift from John, with bloomers puffing out over the cast. Her hair was pigtailed into tight loops around her ears.

In the therapy room, many of the staff had gathered to watch. Other patients—stroke victims, children battling the effects of polio, elderly patients with painful and crippling diseases of the joints, accident victims learning to use prosthetic devices—stopped their own efforts to watch as the attendants stood her between the bars. She looked so tiny, so vulnerable. Her emaciated limbs sticking out from the heavy cast, she seemed no more than thirteen years old.

She stood there, not at all certain she could pass the test. But this is my debut, she reminded herself. All these people have come to see me. She remembered her New York debut, so many years before, how her muscles had frozen in fear, how her stomach had churned, how her feet had felt like chunks of cement, how insufferably heavy her body had seemed.

As her hands clasped the bar for support, she held her head high, refusing to look down at her feet. Not a person in this room was going to know how scared she was. She would appear absolutely confident. That's the secret of dance class; always look like you're the best in the class.

She glanced at the anxious faces around her. They were quiet, intent, hoping, rooting for her. These people need me to succeed, she thought. If I can make it, it'll give them the strength to try. I've got to make it.

But her feet wouldn't move. The signals she had learned to transmit to her muscles were blocked somewhere. Instead of panicking, she imagined a drum beat, then focused on the nursery rhyme tune. "One more step to go . . ."

Her feet began to move, the right foot sliding ahead, the left foot dragging forward, even with the right—then six, eight, twelve inches ahead. Her right foot slid ahead, not stopping

149

alongside the left to stabilize her balance but creeping on ahead, almost as if of its own will.

Slowly, so slowly, she crept and dragged and slid and shuffled and punished herself down that ten-foot track between the bars. It occurred to her that they resembled ballet barres. For just a moment, she was back at the Laurelton School, gripping the barre and trying so hard to follow the other students' feet. She willed her mind back to the therapy room, re-focused on the drum beat, hummed the tune, marched.

She was nearing the end now and had not yet looked down. She wondered if her feet were still following along. There was no feeling left, except an unfamiliar ache starting to build upward from her arches.

She wondered, through the fog in her mind and the insistent beat of her drum, if her orders to her resisting limbs were audible—slide right foot—slide left foot—slide right. . . .

She was only dimly aware that she had reached the end of the track. As her right hand slipped off the end of the bar, she almost fell.

The turning movement was a blessed relief—her left foot and leg didn't have to move. She went through the maneuver she had learned so tediously the night before: Left foot stationary, just slide it around; keep your right foot pivoting. Keep it going, going.

Clinging to the bar with her left hand, she reached across her body with her right, fingers scrabbling for a hold on the opposite bar. It wasn't there! Then, in her haze of fatigue, she realized that she hadn't reached far enough. And there it was! She had it now. Releasing her left hand, she reached blindly behind her for a grip on the opposite rail.

Now she faced back down the way she had come. She had no idea how long it had taken. It could have been minutes or hours.

When she felt her balance secure, she started the long way back down the ten-foot bars. She could no longer see; the sweat of her effort was streaming into her eyes. Somebody gasped. "Look how she's moving. She's almost graceful."

"I can march. See, all of you? I am marching." The words, between clenched teeth, were spoken only for herself. The room was silent, the only sounds the scrape of her feet on the floor.

With five feet to go, all feeling, even the pain, was gone

150

from her legs. There was nothing to connect her to the track she was walking.

"Zephyr," she thought. "I'm flying, just like you. I have pink satin slippers on my feet and I'm soaring over green fields." One hand slid free a second, a small gesture—as if tossing seeds to the birds. It threw her off balance and she fell heavily against the bar.

But before the attendants could reach her, she had regripped the bar, pulled herself upright. Then she had two feet to go, four sliding little steps.

I'm walking home, she said to herself, sliding her right foot forward again. I'm going home to New York.

And then she was at the end. Her feet stopped precisely where she had started so long, long ago. Her head still raised, she met the eyes of those who watched and shared her victory.

Dr. Sam was crying. Dr. Morrison dabbed at his eyes with a handkerchief, muttering over and over, "I can't believe it, but she did it." The patients—the ones who could—were applauding. The others cheered, yelled, making as much noise as they could.

No tears washed Emily's cheeks. She accepted their approval, their love, with a slight, regal nod. "John," she whispered, "I'm coming home. I'm on my way."

12.
Home to Manhattan

There were many people in the lobby to whom she had to say good-bye. They wanted autographs; they wanted one final word; some wanted simply to touch her. All she wanted to do was get it over with.

Then she realized that to these people, her life had meaning. She had changed their lives, and never again would they be the same. This understanding penetrated the weariness of her body and mind, and she was grateful.

Her focus was home. "Please," she asked John. "Run interference for us. We have a plane to catch."

They emerged into the full May bloom of an Indiana spring. She hadn't anticipated the scent of her first unfiltered, unsterile air in over three months. Why, I can smell things growing, she thought. There's a warm breeze. As a child regards a Christmas tree in wonder, she savored the marvels of out-of-doors. I've been hibernating, she thought, just like the bulbs under the ground. And now, just like the flowers, I'm coming out with a new life with its roots in the old. I'm the same person I was before, yet I'm blooming all over again.

The ambulance attendants were lifting her from the wheelchair and placing her on their car's stretcher. A loud voice interrupted her reverie.

"You're the lady we picked up out on the highway in that snowstorm last winter. Wow, worst storm of the year. So, how ya doing?"

"You mean you're the men—this is the same ambulance?"

"Yeah. Funny coincidence, right? We're the guys who brought you in. Now we're the guys who're taking you out. You kept telling us you were gonna dance that night, remember? Never thought we'd see you again."

"Well, here I am, on my way home to dance again."

They drove through an airport gate and onto the runway, pulling up directly alongside the plane. The commercial flight had no facilities for lying down, so Emily was preboarded and strapped into a first-class seat. Despite the long-awaited thrill of going home, the trip was hard. Sitting up for the two hours' flying time, she felt every ripple of the aircraft's motion. Eventually, all the separate discomforts seemed to settle in the pit of her stomach.

"I wish this stomachache would go away," she complained to John. "Isn't it silly, after all I've been through?"

"Em, I'll ask the stewardess if she has anything on board."

"Oh, it's not that bad. I can stand it. Probably just the excitement of going home."

They lived on a street of medium-height buildings, primarily offices and light manufacturing, but with a few storefront businesses and loft residences. Fire trucks and police cars always brought the neighbors to their windows. As the New York ambulance pulled up, all turned out to welcome Emily home, watching, waving, and calling from fire escapes and windows.

As the attendants carried her stretcher up the steps to her front door, it swung open with a flourish, revealing a festive scene of balloons and childishly scrawled banners of welcome. In the door stood little David, his huge blue eyes alight with joy.

She gripped the sides of the stretcher with white knuckles. David's dancing mommy was coming home—flat on her back.

154

Her eyes filled with tears. "Hold on to yourself," the attendant whispered. "You'll frighten him."

He had begun to sing his "Welcome Home, Mommy" song. But he stopped in mid-note, his piping voice quavering off into silence. She reached her emaciated arms toward her son but he backed away. The purple bruises still surrounded her eyes and blotched her cheekbones. Her nose had not healed to its former shape and position. Her unwashed hair was pulled tightly back into pigtails, producing a skeletal look to her face, the left side of which was still partly paralyzed, twisting her smile into an unfamiliar grimace.

"David," John said, "give your mother a kiss."

David was now approaching with wide, frightened eyes.

"It's all right," Emily said softly. "There's plenty of time." She clasped David's hand with as much strength as she could muster. "My darling son, I won't look like this for long. I'm your same Mommy, and pretty soon we'll be playing and singing just like we used to. I'll bet you have a hundred questions you want to ask me. After supper, you can ask me anything you want."

Upstairs, she looked around curiously, hungry for the small details she had thought about for so long. Everything was so clean, so neat. "John," she chuckled, "why didn't you ever tell me about your domestic talents?"

"Well, the maid did most of it." He smiled self-consciously. "I just gave her a few extra things to make it extra nice for you."

The studio had been converted again, this time into a hospital room. There was a rented hospital bed, a wheelchair and crutches in the corner, a bedpan, tray table, and walker. She glanced at the familiar barre and mirrors. "Could you cover up the mirrors, John? I won't be needing them for a while, and I really won't be taking much pleasure in my reflection right now."

Jewish people cover the mirrors after someone has died, she thought, remembering her mother's actions when her father died. And a part of me died in Indianapolis.

On the floor was an air mattress. John explained, "That's where I sleep. You'd better get used to me; I'm not going to leave your side except when I absolutely have to."

She fell quickly asleep and slept soundly, exhausted by

155

the strain and emotions of homecoming. She woke to the sound of rattling dishes in the kitchen. They're hungry, she realized. John and David have had a long day too. And pretty soon John has to leave for the theater.

She swung her legs over the edge of the bed, reached for the walker, and dragged herself to the kitchen.

John glanced up in surprise. "What are you doing out here?"

"I want to make supper for my men."

"You need rest more than we need a supper. I can handle it; I have been for three months. Tomorrow's plenty of time for you to get up and around."

"If you only knew how I've been looking forward to this. It's the one promise I made myself, lying there all those days, that when I got home, the first thing I was going to do was make supper."

John looked at her helplessly. "What are you going to make?"

"One of my specials!"

"I'm not sure I've got much of the food you'll want on hand. We've been eating pretty simple stuff."

"That's why it'll be one of my specials—I'll just use whatever's in the refrigerator. We still have plenty of spices. You can go shopping tomorrow. I'll make out a list tonight."

He realized there was no way for him to force her to go back to bed. Perhaps a quick return to an ordinary way of life was what she needed most. "Okay, Emily. But you've got to let me help. You do the cooking at the stove, and I'll bring you the ingredients."

"One extra-special feast for three, coming right up. We'll all cook this together. Come on David, you can peel the carrots if you're careful. Daddy will cut up the meat for me."

Only later when John was on his way to the theater and David settled in bed, could she relax after the long day. Dragging herself on her walker, she returned to her dance studio hospital bed.

Dr. Benjamin Kalen was one of the most highly respected orthopedic surgeons in New York. Many famous dancers and professional athletes sought him out.

156

Just getting to Kalen's uptown office was a complicated maneuver. A chair elevator had been installed to carry her to the ground floor of their building. Next, she was carried to a chauffeured car by two men. Even now, an automobile ride terrified her. Two more helpers carried her up the stairs to the doctor's office. There she was put in a wheelchair and rolled into the waiting room.

Kalen told her, "I've received your hospital records in the mail. You had a good surgeon in Dr. Morrison. I've heard of his work. My examination and your X rays indicate that everything's coming along as well as can be expected. There's nothing to indicate that you shouldn't be doing physical therapy at home a couple times a week. The nurse will help you locate a good therapist. Do you have any questions?"

She answered, "Just one. You've worked with dancers, and I respect your opinion. Will I be able to dance again?"

"Emily, that's really up to you, your body, and how hard you're willing to work. Mostly the latter."

"I'm willing to work very hard, very hard—if I have the chance to dance again. Do I have a chance?"

"That I can answer. You have a chance, Emily."

She began with Luz Chandler, a handsome woman, athletic, wiry, black Puerto Rican. Luz had a velvet touch, and a stubborn streak to match Emily's own. They started with muscle tests over the entire body, discovering the points of greatest weakness and atrophy. Luz manipulated Emily's limbs, muscle by muscle. As she moved a particular muscle, Emily mentioned its name and how it connected with adjacent muscles.

Luz was delighted. "I can see I'm going to enjoy working with you. Twice a week, isn't that what Dr. Kalen said?"

"I want to work every day, Luz."

"Well, I could come here every other day. Perhaps you could come to the hospital the other days—if I can arrange it. They have the best therapy equipment there."

Well aware she would have to tolerate, on a regular basis, the problems of the car, the attendants, the lifting and carrying, Emily answered quickly, "Yes, Luz. Arrange it. By all means."

157

Emily was tired after Luz left. Exhaustion seemed to be a constant state of existence. John came in with a dinner tray. "While you were working, I fixed you some hamburger with fresh vegetables and a salad. Hope you like it."

"That smells good, John, but I don't really feel like eating right now. Put it in the refrigerator. Maybe I'll just lie here and take a nap. I've got a cramp or something in my stomach."

"After all those exercises you did, I'm not surprised."

"It doesn't feel muscular. But maybe it'll go away pretty soon—I hope."

But it was nearly two hours before the cramp eased and she could relax.

Luz and Emily worked six, often seven, days a week. Sessions grew longer, the routine more varied, as the weeks passed. Luz was a stickler, catching the slightest deviation, correcting even the tiniest mistakes in arm or hand placement, or support positions, lest a mistake became habit.

Every session started with a review, then moved on to a new, more advanced exercise. Emily progressed from exercises on the bed, to work lying on the floor, then lying on her side propped with pillows, and finally standing while holding onto furniture, or bars in the hospital. In the Physical Therapy room, she used weights, bars, and pulleys.

The two women compiled a list of the exercises. Funny names were assigned to each exercise—The Cat, The C, Hurt Your Hams, Foot Roll—and the number of repetitions. Every day, after the supervised session was over, Emily worked on alone, repeating the entire list. It was, as she termed it, her "bedroom barre."

Despite the heavy work schedule, Emily still found it difficult to eat. Kalen, monitoring her in weekly appointments, noticed after eight weeks that she had lost weight, that her cast no longer supported her properly. "You're moving around inside it," he explained. "I'm concerned that may jeopardize the healing in your back.

"I'm going to have you fitted for a Jewett brace. It serves the same function as a cast, but it's more flexible and adapts to changes in your body size."

The new brace—a leather and steel device held together with heavy straps, buckles, and Phillips-head screws, seemed more an instrument of medieval torture than a therapeutic device.

The first night in the brace was a new hell to endure. It was hot, un-airconditioned August weather, and she couldn't sleep.

Though reluctant to complain, Emily spoke out. "John, this is very uncomfortable. It's hurting me. I'm afraid I can't stand it much longer."

"Why didn't you say something, Em? We could have called the doctor. Do you think an aspirin might help?"

"I already took two, and then two more. They're not working. Maybe I should take a Demerol. This is really unbearable."

He brought her the drug, fretted over her. If it was bad enough for his stoic wife to complain, it must be serious.

She lay for an hour, sweat beading her forehead. Again she complained, "John, I don't know if I can keep going. It's getting worse, and the Demerol hasn't helped. I've got to get out of the brace."

He was handy with tools and mechanical devices, enjoyed taking things apart and putting them back together. Yet they wondered—should they, dare they take the brace off? Would it endanger her healing back? At that late hour, there was no one to call for advice.

Emily turned on her side, then rolled back, sweat soaking the pillow. For an hour they put off the decision, John trying to distract her with conversation. She tried to concentrate on the ceiling, the open window, her husband. But the heat and passing time only made the pain less bearable.

John got a screwdriver. Agonizing over each screw, he loosened them by gentle quarter-turns until each was withdrawn from its socket. He laid the two front pieces back, exposing bloody welts where the screws had punctured the skin of collarbone, ribs, and hips. There were small lamb's wool pads beneath each screw, but these hadn't been enough protection for such a slender body.

For an hour she lay with the brace open, stiffly immobile. The hot night air flowed across her skin. It was the first time she had felt a breeze on her body in many months. The relief was exquisite, but it had to end. "I think I can stand it now, John. Let's put me back into my jewelled Jewett bracelet."

"All right, but let me try something. I've got an idea." In

her costume room he found foam rubber, snipped out a piece of double thickness. After washing her wounds, he closed the brace, meticulously aligning the new pads, then turned screws and tightened the straps as tightly as she could bear. At last she could sleep.

The next morning, with Luz, Emily discovered that the brace, though more painful, was lighter than the cast. She could move more easily; her muscles responded faster and more freely.

There were fourteen exercises on the list, dealing with various major muscles. Now, with the brace, the therapist could go on to smaller muscles, harder to identify and isolate: small muscles in the calf, hip, knee to ankle, the adductors and rotators of the legs, as well as muscles of the arms, neck, shoulders, hands, and toes. They also began work on tiny facial muscles, attacking the residual paralysis of her left side, most evident in the left side of her face.

Luz was fascinated by Emily's technique of isolating particular muscles and sending specific signals from her brain. "I suppose I've always done that," Emily said, "but I never really consciously considered how I told a specific muscle to move." The two women sat with their heads together over Emily's anatomy book, studying the neural routes between the brain and every muscle in the body.

Through patience and exhausting work, Emily discovered how to make other muscles do the work of her back. They began to work on her abdominals, even though these large muscles were still trapped in the confines of her Jewett brace. The hip flexors were trained to do some of the work of the abdominals. With Emily lying on her stomach, they started the retraining of her gluteus—careful, dangerous work, for these muscles, if used incorrectly, could endanger her spinal fusion. The new work was grueling. But Emily attacked it energetically. The gluteus muscle provides the foundation for raising the leg into an arabesque.

Recognizing Emily's courage and discipline, Luz drove her patient hard. So one morning she was nonplussed to hear Emily say, "Luz, can we stop now?"

"What's wrong?" Her patient had never wanted to stop before, no matter how painful or tiring the exercise.

"Oh, nothing, I guess. I just feel tired this morning. I didn't sleep well last night."

"Look, quit dancing around me. You're a woman who lives for work. Tell me what's bothering you."

160

"Okay, Luz, I've got a stomachache, just a little one. It doesn't mean anything, except that it makes me feel tired."

"When did the stomachache start?"

"Last night. I thought it stopped but it started again right after breakfast."

Luz's expert fingers probed beneath the brace, but Emily didn't react. "Do you think I could have strained a weak muscle in the new exercise yesterday? Before I went to bed I did thirty repetitions."

"That wouldn't give you a stomachache this morning," Luz answered. "Have you ever felt this particular pain before?"

"I have a couple of times. It always goes away."

Luz glanced at her sharply. "Well, let's give you a rest now and no exercises until the stomachache goes away. If this pain flares up again, you'd better call your doctor. Don't take any chances, okay?"

The stomachache lasted almost three hours.

By the end of the summer Emily could walk easily with crutches, and short distances unsupported. It was really more of a shuffle than a walk. When she wanted to get someplace in a hurry, she would swing along on her crutches. But she *was* walking on her own. She began to listen to her tapes for pleasure.

And John had some good news of his own. "I've got a movie, Emily. I'm supposed to call my agent tomorrow, but they've already completed the preliminary negotiations. It's my first major role—" He noticed his wife's face, taut with pain. "Em, what's the matter?"

"It's my stomach. It's hard to get a breath."

John picked her up and carried her to the bed. Stretching out provided only minimal relief.

She worked her fingers under the the brace. "You'd better call Dr. Albertson. He's got all my pre-accident case history. I feel a sharp point like a needle in my stomach. It really hurts."

"It could be something related to her abdominal surgery," their family doctor said. "Have her lie as still as possible. If the pain doesn't lessen in a reasonable time, say a couple of hours, call me back. Otherwise, I can come by late this afternoon after office hours."

The pain subsided by evening, but the sharp point remained. "In the operation immediately following the accident," Dr. Tim Albertson said, "they used metal stitches to sew you together. One of the stitches has popped and the sharp end is sticking out, just below the surface of the skin."

"Is that serious?" Emily asked.

"Not at all. Come into my office in the morning. I'll give you a local anesthetic, then make a small incision and remove the piece of wire. It's a fairly simple procedure and you should be able to continue your exercise program with your therapist in a day or so."

Emily glanced at John. "I guess this solves the problem of those cramps I've been getting. That little piece of wire must have been floating around in there and every once in a while, when I'd move wrong, it would poke me."

"You mean you've been having stomach cramps on some sort of a regular basis?" Albertson asked.

"Yes. Not bad, though. And pretty infrequently. I'm sure the stitch was the cause."

"Were the cramps general or in one specific spot?"

"They were pretty specific. Right about where you found the stitch poking out. So now you've found the answer."

The operation to remove the offending stitch went smoothly. Afterward Albertson said, "Emily, you should have reported the problem before this. Somebody who's been through what you've been through can't be too careful."

"Of course you're right, Dr. Albertson. But you know how I hate to complain."

"Emily, starting right now, learn to complain a little. You're not out of the woods yet, you know. If the pain flares up again, let me know immediately."

Gradually, Emily was released from the Jewett's embrace. First for an hour a day, then two, then three. Then the doctors said she could sleep without it, eat without it, take a shower. What a day that was, her first shower in seven months. From the shower stall she called her son. "David, get the camera please."

He brought the family's camera, opened the bathroom door, and handed the camera in.

"David, I want a souvenir of this day. Come on in, somebody has to take the picture, and it has to be you."

He entered, eyes wide at the surgical scars on his mother's body. He asked many questions, and she patiently described each operation. He was particularly fascinated by the idea of steel wires holding his mother together.

"But Mommy," he worried, "people are all wet inside. Won't you rust?"

Feeling stronger, she began to wear the brace only during her exercise periods which, by then, were lasting most of the day. Luz's original list of 14 exercises had lengthened to 115. Four times a day Emily worked through the long list. She began after breakfast, going through the entire 115 in preparation for Luz's visit. Then she did them again with her therapist. After a rest period and lunch, she repeated the series, finally performing the entire list once again after dinner, while John was at the theater.

She received Luz's permission to begin limited dance exercises at her barre. She wasn't allowed jumps, turns, or torso bends, but she could try splits and extensions, *pliés, tendu, passes.*

With Luz's knowledge, but without Kalen's permission because she was certain it would worry him, she returned to ballet class with Nenette Charisse.

Her teacher and the other dancers were first stunned, then fascinated as they watched Emily, braced in metal and leather, moving with increasing grace and suppleness. Over the weeks they gradually began to ask questions, and Emily named and described each muscle, demonstrated exercises for strengthening specific muscles, explained her techniques of sending signals to isolate and activate certain areas of her body.

Her face had returned to normal. The stitches had been removed. Nature erased the dark bruises. As her exercise program

163

restored mobility and control, her residual paralysis diminished, though certain muscles, because of the fusion, massive abdominal surgery, and the paralysis, did not attain full function. Emily discovered alternative ways to produce certain movements, small compensations which even dancers could not discern.

Yet she could not gain weight. She remained well below her former size. Emily attributed it to her extraordinary work schedule. I like being so thin, she told herself cheerfully. I'll think about eating and building up my strength once I start rehearsals again.

The night before John was to leave for Hollywood, she had another stomachache. They went through the list of foods she had eaten during the day and could find nothing unusual.

"Look, John, don't worry about it. If you don't mind cleaning up the kitchen and getting David ready for bed, I think I'll nap while you're at the rehearsal. I'll be okay by the time you get home."

When he came in, he found his wife lying on her side, curled around a pillow.

"It's—it got pretty bad this evening," she said. "But it's beginning to ease up now."

"Is it another stitch?"

"No. It's nothing like I felt before. The pillow seems to help. Do you think, maybe, I could have an ulcer?"

"I think we'd better call Albertson."

"No, don't. It's too late. The pain's easing. I'll call his office in the morning."

The pain had lasted four hours. She knew, because she had timed it.

Packing the next morning, John asked, "Have you called Albertson yet?"

"It's nothing to bother him with. Everybody gets stomachaches."

"Not as frequently as you've been getting them. I'm going to the Coast for two months. If you won't call the doctor, I will."

"If it recurs, I'll call Albertson, I promise."

"No, Emily. I want him to look at you before I leave for the airport. Just to ease my mind."

John made the call, and Albertson made room for Emily

164

on his afternoon schedule. He, too, suspected an ulcer, and put her through a full series of gastrointestinal tests. When the test results came back with no evidence of ulcer, John was satisfied, and he was on his way.

Through October and into November's bleak cold, she continued to progress. Luz came only once a week, still supervising her patient's development. Proudly, Emily would demonstrate her new ideas and strengths for Luz.

"When dancers perform an arabesque, they arch from the waist. The balance center is so important. But my back is permanently straight, so I've learned to arch from my hips. My arabesque looks just as good as it ever did. And look," she added proudly, beginning a slow-motion nose dive to the floor, "I'm learning, one more time, how to do a *penché arabesque.*"

She began preparing to dance again. Her tapes of her repertory for symphonies came out of their boxes. Once again music filled her studio, and she called Ron, her agent.

"I was thinking that I'd like to start my latest comeback off-off-off-off Broadway, *way* off Broadway. So far away that if I had problems, it wouldn't affect my chances back in New York."

"That's probably a good idea, Emily. But not yet. Next year, maybe."

"Ron, I'd like to try to get a tour of Europe or the Far East—that's off-off Broadway, for the summer maybe. Let me borrow your letterhead and write the letters myself. You know, that's the way I used to do it a long time ago."

"Well, if you want to make the effort, by all means—use our stationery." His tone of voice clearly indicated that he was humoring her.

To her daily routine of exercise work was now added the task of drafting "Harriet Schaeffer" letters, seeking bookings. She wrote to Guam, Hong Kong, Manila, Buenos Aires, Johannesburg, Sydney, Vienna; anywhere she could find a potential sponsor for a dance concert.

In John's absence, she put in eight- and ten-hour work days. As she worked, she played her symphonies—no longer as background music. She began to review her old choreography notes, looking for changes that would avoid dangerous off-balance turns and high acrobatic jumping with their attendant risk of falls.

One afternoon, after the weekly talk and work session with Luz, Emily played the Mahler for her therapist.

When the symphony was finished, they were both in tears.

"I knew you'd understand what the music means," Emily said. "I just needed somebody to share it with me. Luz, I was on my way to dance to that music when I had my accident. I want to do it again. That symphony touches me more now than ever.

"Mahler died fairly young, and he knew his death was coming and he feared it, yet his symphony is full of affirmation, the triumph over death. You can hear it. That's why we cry when we hear the music. That's why I have to dance the Mahler. He is saying in music what I've learned from this accident experience. Will you help me, Luz?"

"Emily, with your artistry, you can tell your story; you can do what most people only dream of doing—expressing what they really feel. I think you can do it without my help, but I'll be glad to help you any way I can."

Around midnight, Emily awoke. Pain was ravaging her stomach. She glanced at the clock, wondering how long it would last this time. She lay flat, resisting the impulse to curl around a pillow, fearful that any movement would increase the pain.

She used one of her hospital tricks: resisting pain by concentrating on the passage of time. The pain intensified and ebbed at fairly precise intervals. She began timing the pains.

Perhaps a pill would help. Unable to stand upright, she dragged herself to the bathroom medicine cabinet, hauled herself upright by clinging to the basin, and swallowed a Demerol. She debated for a moment, then took another.

When the two pills brought no respite, she returned to the cabinet and took four aspirins. Next she tried a 10-milligram tablet of Valium, washed down with a glass of Alka-Seltzer. But the

166

pain went on. What can I do? she asked herself. I've taken too many pills already, and they haven't done any good. All I can do is wait it out.

Hoping to relieve the pressure, she tried vomiting by sticking her finger down her throat, but nothing happened. She noticed that her stomach seemed to be bloated. The pressure increased, the pain coming in shorter intervals.

She swallowed more of the assortment of pills the Indianapolis doctors had prescribed for her back surgery pain. My stomach's all swollen, and the pains are worse. I can't feel any loose stitches. What can be wrong with me?

Trying not to writhe on the bed, she moaned, "John, please help me." Then she remembered John was still in California. He couldn't come.

She determined to hold out for four hours—the length of her last attack. She concentrated on the hands' slow sweep around the clock face, anticipating a release. When it didn't happen, she picked up the telephone.

"I'm sorry to have to call in the middle of the night, Dr. Albertson," she said. "But my stomachache is back. I can't sleep. I was hoping you could prescribe something."

"Have you taken anything?"

"Yes." She couldn't remember exactly what, so she rattled off the names on the bottles in her medicine cabinet.

"I see." He asked her to describe the pain. She tried to concentrate, be precise, using medical terminology rather than adjectives.

"I think I'd better come to Manhattan and take a look at you. Can you get to a hospital?"

"Of course."

"All right, go to Roosevelt. I'll met you at the Emergency Room." And he hung up.

How will I get to the hospital? she wondered. Somebody has to take me. But how can I get an ambulance to come? She thought of calling Dr. Albertson back, but decided she didn't want to bother him. Slowly she reached for the yellow pages, searching for the "Ambulance Services" heading. But her eyes wouldn't focus on the numbers. She managed to discern the exchange, then transferred her attention to the telephone dial, slowly inserting her finger and dialing. Then she had to refocus her eyes on the listing, try to make out the last four digits.

Finally—it seemed as if a great deal of time had passed—she heard the phone ringing at the other end. "All our ambulances are out on call now. It's a bad night for traffic accidents," said the man who answered. "I'm sorry, ma'am." Thanking him, she hung up.

Now what am I to do? I must get to the hospital. Dr. Albertson is expecting me. But her eyes felt heavy. She wanted to go to sleep. If I can go to sleep now, she thought, maybe the pain will be gone when I wake up. But a fresh spasm brought her attention back. Was this one worse than the last? She didn't know; she had lost the ability to judge. Perhaps the police could help her.

She had written her precinct number inside the front cover of the phone book in large numbers, and it was easy to find. The officer who answered was sympathetic, but the hospital she wanted to go to was out of their precinct. He advised her to call Roosevelt. He had to repeat the number several times, and slowly she managed to write it down. Haltingly, at times incoherently, Emily managed to convey her need to the operator at Roosevelt.

"We aren't allowed to send our ambulances into your district, ma'am. You'll have to call a private ambulance service. Your neighborhood emergency hospital is St. Vincent's."

"But, please, I already tried an ambulance service. All their ambulances were out. Can't you help me?"

"Call St. Vincent's," the woman suggested. "I think they have some available." She gave Emily the number. But after hanging up the phone, Emily couldn't decipher what she had written.

She lay her head back on the pillow. Unconsciousness swept over her. It seemed so simple to just let go. But the pain, still increasing in intensity, dragged her back unwillingly. I've never, never canceled a booking, she thought. If they won't come and get me, well, then I must go myself.

Trying to select an outfit to wear seemed insurmountable. She gave up on that and headed for the stairs wearing only her nightgown, bathrobe, and slippers. I must be careful; I don't have my brace on, she thought, clinging to the elevator seat that had been installed to carry her up and down stairs, then inching along the

168

floor at the landing. The front door seemed too heavy to budge, but she gathered what little strength she had left and produced a gap she could slide through. She inched down the steps to the street, covered with an early-winter dusting of snow.

She leaned her hot forehead against the cool bricks of the wall. Did I leave the door open? David was asleep inside, alone. But climbing back up the front steps was too much. I must get help. I can get a taxi at Fifth Avenue.

Doubled over with cramps, she began to shuffle up the street toward the corner.

At the corner, she peered through falling snow, leaning against a light pole. I must find a taxi, she thought. I must not fall asleep here. That's my assignment—get a cab. She waved her arm at random, hoping someone would see.

An off-duty cab pulled over, the driver seeing that something was wrong. She leaned helplessly against the rear door. "Just pull, lady," he yelled from inside, "It's open. Just pull the handle."

She managed to get into the warm back seat and sank back into the cushions. It had been such a long trip, and she was so tired.

"Hey, lady, you sick or somethin'? Where to?"

She barely heard the question, knew she must answer him. But she couldn't remember. "The hospital . . . My son . . ."

"Okay, lady. But which one's your son in? Which hospital?"

"Not—my son, me. I'm sorry, I seem to have forgotten."

"St. Vincent's is near here. Is that the one?"

Poor little David, alone in the house. The driver has to know where I'm to go. She concentrated, trying to break through the gauzy curtain of pain medication. "Please, I'm trying to remember. . . . The doctor said—"

"Ma'am, how about Roosevelt? It's not far."

"Roosevelt? Yes. Take me—wherever you just said."

At Roosevelt's Emergency Room, Albertson had been waiting. He hurried over to her.

She wanted to help the doctors diagnose her, but she kept falling asleep in mid-answer. After too many pills and worn down by the pain, she didn't really care what happened to her anymore.

Albertson asked, "What did you take for the pain?"

169

"I can't remember," she answered. "But—please call John, tell him. And David, he's alone. Help him, please." She wished they'd do whatever they had to do and leave her in peace.

Albertson noted her pulse rate was slowing; her blood pressure was 55 over 80, and dropping. Her chilled body temperature had been 95° when the attendants got her out of the cab and into Emergency. It dropped another degree in the first hour. The medical investigative procedure began, along with the attachment of life-support equipment that had already become necessary.

At one point, she struggled up through the fog into the blur of activity around her and asked why they were doing all these things. "Emily," Albertson explained, "we're going to have to operate on you. But first we have to find out what's wrong."

"Please—call John. He has to get our son."

They knew only that he was in California, making a movie. She instructed them to call her neighbor, ask the man to enter Emily's home and look up John's number on her Rolodex.

"Does your neighbor have a key?" they asked. "How can he get in?"

She thought a long time; they feared she was unconscious. "I think . . . yes, I think I left the door open. And this is important," she whispered, "ask my neighbor to get somebody to take care of David."

Through the night they worked to keep her alive, to identify the trouble. Unconscious most of the time, Emily was able to supply only a few clues.

Albertson called Dr. Jerry Trent, Roosevelt's chief of surgery, into consultation, and rapped out the symptoms: "Markedly distended abdomen. Tympanic sounds and blood count indicating intestinal impairment. Elevated white cell blood count. Weak peripheral pulse." Lab tests were run; results analyzed and calculated. The two doctors decided to perform a barium swallow X ray as Trent hurried off to his first scheduled operation of the day.

"Emily, can you hear me?" Albertson asked.

She didn't respond.

"Emily!" he insisted. "Listen to me. We must have your permission to operate. You must answer me."

After a long time, she moved her head slightly. "Oper-

170

ate?" He was such a kind man, but she had been enough trouble already. "It doesn't hurt anymore. You can stop worrying."

"Emily. You must sign this form." He thrust a piece of paper in front of her.

"I—don't want . . . any more operations. I've had . . . enough."

"We have to take you to surgery, Emily."

"John, does he know?"

"Yes. We talked to him. He's on his way back to New York."

"David? Is he . . . all right . . .?"

"Your neighbor's staying in your house with David to-night. Now sign this form so we can take care of you. Please?"

Dr. Albertson was asking so politely. He was such a nice man. If it would make him happy, if he would go away and let her rest. She signed his paper.

The sense of movement stirred her. She opened her eyes. They were rolling her down the hallway on a surgical cart. Funny, she thought, I feel like I'm floating. And I can't feel any pain— Thank you, God, for taking the pain away.

When the cart stopped, she opened her eyes again and tried to look around her. How funny, she thought, this doesn't look like the operating rooms in the movies. She decided the brown wooden walls, student chairs, lights overhead, looked like one of a thousand high school auditoriums in which she'd done so many, many one-night stands.

She somehow associated those vague faces around her with her performance. Why are they so busy? she wondered. They don't have to rush so. I'm too tired to dance. I think I'll just go to sleep now. She tried to tell them. It's okay, fellows. I'm not going to do the performance tonight.

She took one last look around her and remembered a line from some poem, "This is the way the world ends." How nice, restful, to simply go off to sleep. David's taken care of; John's taken care of. Now I can let go. . . .

13.
Roosevelt Hospital

The telephone rang in Roosevelt Hospital's surgical amphitheater. "Dr. Trent," a nurse said, "Dr. Albertson says his patient you saw this morning is now a red blanket. He wants to operate immediately and would like you to handle the surgery."

"Tell Dr. Albertson I'll be about ten minutes here."

Albertson was waiting in the scrub room when Trent finished.

"That woman we saw this morning?" Trent asked.

"Right. We completed the diagnosis about an hour ago. The barium swallow shows what we suspected, a strangulated small intestine. Because of the time elapsed since the onset of the symptoms, I suspect massive involvement.

"Also her electrocardiogram shows atrial-tachycardia and nonspecific myocardial alteration. Her condition is marginally stable, but tenuous. It's going to be complicated, and that's why I want the best surgeon in this city. That's you, Jerry."

173

"All right, start prepping her."

"She's already prepped and waiting in O.R. One."

"Okay, You start the laparotomy. I'll meet you in there in a moment or two."

Emily was quickly connected to the monitoring machines. The anesthetist did his work swiftly, puncturing the inside of her forearm with the long intravenous needle and clamping the nose cone over her face. The head surgical nurse laid out the instruments while an assistant arranged the surgical drape, exposing her stomach area, swabbing with disinfectant.

Albertson pinked the breastbone-to-navel incision line along the healed scar from her Indianapolis surgery. He scalpeled through the skin, then through the heavy abdominal muscles, tying off veins and arteries, clamping back the envelopes of flesh on either side.

Trent walked in. "What have we got?"

"Secondary volvulus, gangrene involving practically the entire small intestine. See here? Dilatation of the small intestine with a narrowing in the proximal jejunum. It's twisted around the adhesions from the previous surgery. We'll have to do a complete resection. There isn't much left to save."

"Well, then, we'll save as much as we can," Trent said briskly, moving into position and reaching for the instrument tray.

A sudden noise froze Trent. The heart monitoring machine had changed from its reassuring "beep . . . beep . . . beep" sound to a single loud tone. Rather than the moving parabolas indicating normal heart function, the oscilloscope displayed a clean straight line.

"Zero pulse," the anesthetist rapped out. Suddenly the line of the "scope" began bouncing crazily across the screen. "She's fibrillating," he called.

A nurse handed the defibrillator pads to Trent as Albertson swabbed electrical contact ointment on either side of her chest. Trent pressed the pads to her body and ordered, "Stand back. Hit it."

The machine hummed, Emily's body convulsed. The monitor's white dot smoothed momentarily, then resumed its crazed dance across the screen. "Five hundred," Trent called. "Hit it." Once again the inert form on the table jerked.

174

"I'm getting a pulse now," the anesthetist announced. The monitor display changed as the heart's frantic convulsions settled into a rapid, but steady, beat. It had been nearly five minutes.

"All right, little lady," Trent muttered quietly. "Let's not have any more of that, okay?"

Trent plunged both hands into her intestinal cavity, deftly separating the coils of intestine. He glanced at Albertson. "It looks like about four feet of the jejunum and a few inches of the ileum are not involved."

"Enough for an anastomosis of the jejunum to the ascending colon?" Albertson asked.

"I think so. Let's hope so, for her sake."

The two surgeons went to work with scalpels and clamps. Again the anesthetist's urgent voice interrupted them. "She's going again. I'm losing pulse. Blood pressure at twenty-five over forty and dropping fast." The monitor again began its ominous, uninterrupted tone.

An assistant had the pads in Trent's hands before he could ask for them. "Give her four hundred." The heart continued its manic dash from life. Trent ordered an increase in the charge. An assistant spun the dials, pressed the button. "Come on, baby, come on," Trent pleaded, bearing down hard with the pads. "Don't go away from us now."

The oscilloscope line jumped crazily, then faded to a straight line.

"No vital signs," the anesthetist reported.

"Goddammit. No!" Albertson reached to pound her chest.

"Wait," Trent ordered. "Let's try another shock. Give it one thousand."

Her body twisted violently, arching off the table in the convulsion. The warning tone continued.

Albertson said, "Open-heart massage. Let's open her up."

"No time," Trent countermanded. "Try two thousand. Jolt her again."

The machine hummed. Again her body convulsed at the surge of electricity. The surgical team was rewarded with a beat from her heart—then another, and finally a rapid, unnatural rhythm.

"Let's work fast, Jerry, or the next time we'll lose her. Do you think we should take the whole small intestine?"

"No, I can save what's still functioning, and the valve between the jejunum and ileum. That'll give her some chance at a normal life."

"*If* she gets out of here alive!" Albertson argued. "But the anastomosis will take a few hours. I don't think she can take that much more."

"Come on, Tim, we owe her a chance to function normally."

"But she's gone out twice now, five minutes each time. With that much oxygen deprivation, she could have brain damage anyway. What difference will it make?"

"Tim," Trent said firmly, "you asked me in here. So I'm going to complete the procedure the best way I know how. I don't want to be responsible for condemning her to an invalid's existence in a nursing home."

Trent worked as quickly as possible connecting the valve to the remaining jejunum—but not quick enough to avoid another onset of fibrillation. "I told you so," Albertson muttered underneath his breath. But once again, the charge of electricity brought her heart back into a precarious, but steady, rhythm.

John arrived while Emily was still in the recovery room. It seemed so frighteningly like Indianapolis all over again. It didn't help that Albertson, their family physician and longtime friend, didn't know how to begin.

"John, I want to be as positive as I can, but at the same time I think you must know her heart stopped three times during the surgery."

"Where is she?" John asked. "Please, I have to see her."

Against all hospital procedure, he was allowed into the recovery room. There his wife lay, ghostly pale and unmoving, plugged by webs of tubing into a myriad of machines and devices. Occasional frowns creased her forehead. She muttered unintelligible words. Reassured that at least she was alive, John was ushered out.

"She's technically listed in critical condition," Albertson explained. "But over the last couple of hours since the operation, she

176

has stabilized. Blood pressure, pulse rate, and her temperature all seem to be returning to normal. Both the machines and staff are monitoring her constantly. If there's the slightest change, we have resuscitation equipment standing by."

"But she *will* live?"

"Chances are, yes. But what's in doubt is the *quality* of that life. There's a possibility of brain damage. When the heart stops, the supply of oxygen to the brain is cut off. Each time Emily's heart stopped, it took five minutes or a little longer to get it started again. Five minutes is considered the longest the brain can go without oxygen before suffering irreversible cell damage. Her heart was stopped for a total of over 15 minutes, spread over the three occurrences."

"Oh, God," John groaned.

"It's simply too early for us to tell how she'll react. We'll just have to wait for her to regain consciousness so we can run some tests. She was lucky Dr. Trent was able to save as much of the intestine as he did. Total resection would have meant she would be confined to a nursing home or hospital the rest of her life. And under those conditions she probably wouldn't have lived very long."

"And now?" John asked dully. "What kind of future does she have?"

"Certainly she'll need a very special diet. The remaining portion of intestine is quite narrow, so she'll have to be careful not to eat anything that's bulky and difficult to digest. Otherwise, she could have a recurrence and we'll have to take out the rest. There's even a possibility that she might have to be on intravenous feeding for a long time, possibly the rest of her life. But again, we just don't know. When she begins to recover from the surgery, we'll begin a series of tests that will help us plan her future."

"If she has a future, Tim."

John couldn't rid himself of his blacker thoughts. How many blows can one small woman take before she gives up? This is the last straw. Though Albertson told him it would be several hours before Emily would leave the recovery room, John refused to leave the hospital. Once again, he could do nothing but wait and chain-smoke.

Nine hours after she had left the operating room, Emily was taken upstairs to Intensive Care, where she was again plugged into the electronic network. John was allowed to remain by her bedside.

At the first slight flickering of her eyelids, he was up and at her side. As her eyes focused, she smiled wanly at him. "Hello, dear."

Anxiously, he asked, "What's your name?"

The question perplexed her. "My name is Emily, of course. What's the matter with you?"

"What's *my* name? Where do we live?"

"John, please stop it. What is wrong with you?" Much too tired to play games, she was getting very cross. But then she smiled; he had brought her such a beautiful flower.

"Darling, what a huge flower! It's such a bright orange. Where did you find it?"

He glanced around in confusion. There were no flowers in Intensive Care.

"Right there on my wall, behind you. A giant flower, with gloriously bright petals. It's so dazzling it almost hurts my eyes."

He looked where she indicated, saw only a reflection of the late afternoon sun streaming in the windows.

"Emily, are you sure you're all right? What's our son's name?"

"David. Look, why are you asking me all these silly questions? I'm fine. Most of the pain is gone. The operation must have gone all right. And please don't talk so loud. I can hear."

John thought he had been talking fairly quietly. Maybe not. He told her what had happened in the operating room, glancing involuntarily at the heart monitoring machine, fearful that the news would shock her.

It didn't. Instead, she was very articulate. "I remember coming here through the snow, in a taxi I think. Then it was such a long time. Doctors kept poking me and testing me and asking me questions. Finally I got them to tell me that you and David were taken care of."

"Your only concern was about David and me?"

"Yes. Then my last job was finished, you see? Then I was content. I was ready to die."

In his extreme relief that his wife was alive, John laid his

178

head next to hers on the pillow and wept silently. She ran her fingers through his hair.

"It was so easy, just like going to sleep. But oh John, I remember having such an awful nightmare. There was this strange sound, a steady tone, and people were shouting and hitting at me, and the sound just went on and on. Then it stopped."

"Your heart stopped, Em. That was the sound of the heart monitor. Did you see anything strange, visions, like those people we keep reading about?"

"I don't know what I saw, John. Or even if I 'saw' anything. All I know is that I don't feel like I'm the same person I was yesterday. Sounds odd, doesn't it? I'm not even sure what I mean by that. Let me sort it all out, then I'll talk about it. Anyway, there are some important things we have to do.

"Please call Ron for me. Make sure my bookings are okay. His number is 243-1787. Don't tell him what happened to me. I don't want anybody to find out and cancel my appearances. And call Luz, at, let's see, her number is Trafalgar 7-6225. Ask her not to come in until I let her know.

"When you go home, pay the power bill that's on my desk. Remember, it comes out of the corporate account. The amount was, I think, $68.19. Yes, that's it. And please run by David's nursery school. That's at 422 Greenwich, the new building, next to the Treasurehouse Restaurant. He left his coat there yesterday. And—"

John had been listening in amazement. "Whoa, honey, wait a minute. I can't remember all these numbers."

"Well, get a pencil and paper. We're out of milk and hamburger. Better pick some up. And some butter, too."

On his way to the telephone, he ran into Dr. Albertson in the hall. "John, have you talked with Emily yet? Is she making any sense?"

"She's making too much sense," John answered. "She seems to have total recall of little things—telephone numbers, amounts of bills, addresses. It's uncanny. She was never absentminded, she just never bothered with those kind of details. She'd make lists to remind herself of things to do. She's the type who used

179

the Rolodex for phone numbers instead of memorizing them. And you say she could be brain-damaged?

"Another thing," he continued. "Her senses seem super-acute. Like I'm talking in a normal tone of voice, and she says I'm too loud. She says she can hear the rhythms of the machines in the room, and the intravenous dripping. And she says the colors are so intense they hurt her eyes. Is it possible that the lack of oxygen intensified her brain processes? Or what if she's like a lightbulb that flares before it goes out? Is that possible?"

The doctor said, "Maybe it's a psychological reaction to coming so close to death. Perhaps increased brain activity occurs after such an episode. It could taper off anytime. We just don't know."

"So you think there's still the possibility of brain damage?"

"We'll watch her and see what happens over the next few weeks."

"Will it be that long before she can go home?"

"She'll be here a minimum of six weeks. She's so weak, she won't be ready to get out of that bed for five or six days anyway."

The next day, John returned to her side. "Did you do all those things I asked you to do, honey?" she asked. "Sorry you had to get stuck with all the errands."

"I got most of them done." he said. "Except I couldn't get Ron. I left a message with his answering service asking him to call back."

"Oh, damn. That's the most important one. I can't risk having any bookings canceled. I'll tell him I had my appendix out. I'll be out of the hospital in a week."

"A week! That's crazy. Dr. Albertson says it'll be more like six weeks. You're not even going to move out of that bed for a week."

"Nonsense. I'll go call him myself. We can't take a chance that he'd call at home and not get us. Now come on, help me get out of this bed."

John was overwhelmed by this dynamo before him. "Em, there's no phone in Intensive Care."

"There's a phone booth in the corridor outside. I know; I've heard people using it." She pointed to the intravenous stand by her bed. "Now you just grab that pole and come on. Roll it alongside me while I walk."

She rolled onto her side and studied the heart monitoring machine. Carefully, she reached for the wires and unplugged herself.

"Hey, *whoa!*"

"Have you got a dime?" She slid her legs over the side of the bed and stepped gently onto the floor. "Let's go call Ron.

Two weeks to the day after they brought Emily into Roosevelt's emergency room, John had to return to California. Emily discharged herself. She wound an Ace bandage around her stomach and walked out the front door, hailed a taxi, and went home.

She wasn't home very long before the phone rang. It was John, calling long-distance. "I called the hospital just now and they said you'd signed yourself out. What in the world do you think you're doing?"

"Well, you know Dr. Albertson said I'm healing just fine. He said from now on all I really needed is bed rest. And I can get that here at home as well as in the hospital."

"Emily, you had major surgery two weeks ago. You almost died. Let yourself be coddled for a while."

"I *will* take it easy," she answered. "I won't work out until Luz is here to supervise. And the housekeeper kept the house so neat that there isn't any housework for me to do. I'll recover faster at home, being with David, doing little things, keeping busy.

"Believe me, I'm learning what I can do and what I can't.

"Dr. Albertson and I worked out a diet. There are a lot of foods that I won't be able to eat anymore. But there are a lot of foods that I *can* eat, too, and a liquid diet supplement to keep up my strength when I go back to work. Work is what I'm looking forward to. I can't wait to call Luz and make an appointment."

"Just promise me you'll take it easy," John said.

"I will. Now, if you're finished lecturing me, I've got to move the piano in the studio, take a barre, practice my jumps, go outside and shovel the snow. . . ."

He sighed.

"Honestly, Em, sometimes I think you *are* brain-damaged—but it happened years ago. I think *I'm* brain-damaged after putting up with you all these years."

She had to start all over again. During the laparotomy, the surgeons had cut all the major abdominal muscles. Without abdominal strength, the problems of her fused spine were insurmountable. For two weeks she confined herself to exercises of the feet, legs, arms, neck, and face, waiting for the abdominals to heal.

Finally she called Luz and the two began abdominal exercises—only small movements at first, so as not to endanger the still-healing flesh.

But Emily was encouraged. That night, to celebrate, she fixed a bowl of popcorn and had a party with David.

Forty-five minutes later the stomachache returned. She timed the peristaltic pains, then called Albertson. He ordered her back to the hospital and met her in Emergency. But the pains receded, then disappeared.

Before discharging her, Albertson said, "Emily, you got a reprieve. But I have to tell you that any more of these recurrences could be fatal, or at least permanently incapacitating. Now, popcorn is definitely *not* on your list of permitted foods. This is a warning—stick to the diet I gave you or you'll be back in here again."

With Albertson's permission, Luz and Emily began careful muscle-testing. The first problem was the abdominals—a trial roll-up into the position of the letter "C."

Emily readied herself, controlling her breathing as she had been taught, then raised her head a few inches. She sent a signal to her shoulders and upper torso to follow, but nothing happened. She tried again, and failed. A third attempt was equally fruitless.

"It's no good," she gasped, slumping back against the floor. "I guess the muscles haven't healed much."

"All right," Luz ordered, "we go back to the beginning. I'll serve as your abdominal muscles." She positioned herself behind her patient, as Emily raised her head and began lifting. With Luz's help, she was able to roll into the "C" position. But as she rolled up, the long row of metal stitches splicing her navel pulled and stretched her damaged flesh.

"Wait a minute, Luz. That hurts. Oh, Luz, I'm terrified of that pain." She lay back down on the floor sweating. The muscles she had so carefully strengthened to support her stiffened spine were now gone.

"Okay, Luz. I've got the old list of exercises you gave me. I'll just have to go back to the first one and go from there."

She arranged pillows on the floor, then stretched out, propping her shoulders against the pillow. Getting her stomach muscles accustomed to the slightly painful flexed position was a start.

Gradually she extended her time on the pillows—a painless minute, then four minutes of pain; three minutes of comfort, then five minutes of strain. In her stationary position, she tried to activate the abdominals as Luz had taught her, visualizing the ring of muscles gradually tightening around her navel.

As she grew used to the position, she dispensed with the pillows, propping herelf on her elbows instead. Ever so slowly, she began to transfer her torso's weight from her elbows to her abdominal muscles. Through a period of days, she took away half an elbow's support on one side, then half an elbow's support on the other. Then a whole elbow on one side, and finally the other, until she was able to hold herself in the "C" position solely with her re-activated stomach muscles. Then she was able to begin practicing the roll-up. She gained a bare inch or so a day, but eventually rolled herself up into a perfect "C," then back down again, in control all the way.

Within a month, she and Luz had restored the entire sequence of 114 exercises. Emily was working through the list four times a day.

During the four weeks, the intestinal blockage recurred. Once again she timed the pains and went to the hospital when her clock told her it was time. Once again, the blockage cleared itself.

"Do these blockages keep occurring because of my exercises?" she asked Dr. Albertson.

"No, the more exercise you do, the better off you'll be. Just remember to adhere to the diet; that's the critical element."

"That diet! Dr. Albertson, I'm getting tired of eating cheese and hamburger and the liquid diet supplement! I fix regular meals for David and everything smells so good, and then I sit down to the same old boring thing. And I seem to be hungry all the time."

"It's one manifestation of your condition. What you have

to do is eat seven or eight small meals a day. And stick with the diet. Have you been taking your pills every day?"

"Twelve pills three times a day."

"I'm afraid that you're going to have to live with that."

"All right, then I'll live with it."

She got books on diet, carbohydrates, calories, fiber content of foods, metabolism, the digestive system. Emily even read the fad books on Oriental herbs, special teas, super vitamins. Like a medical student, she studied books on endocrinology, the liver, all aspects of her condition both in the present, and what she could expect in the future.

When the telephone rang, she was in the middle of her exercise routine. There were times when she ignored a ringing telephone, reasoning that people determined to talk to her would call back. But that insistent ring, and some curiosity, prevailed. It was her agent.

"Just calling to see how you're getting along without an appendix."

"Well, frankly, Ron, it was a little worse than an appendix. A lot worse. I'm sorry I had to lie to you, but I was afraid you'd try to convince me to cancel my bookings. I couldn't have stood that."

"But what happened?"

"It's too complicated to go into right now. Besides, it's all over and I'm healthy again. The important thing is that I took a limited barre yesterday, and a few dance steps. And I've been listening to my old music, too."

"You haven't been listening to Mahler's Fifth Symphony by any chance?"

"Yes, I have, as a matter of fact. Why?"

"Well, my dear, I have a little surprise for you. I had a call this morning from the City Symphony people. They want to get the contracts signed and finalize their plans for you to do the Mahler with them."

"When Maestro Schiff sent me that telegram in Indianapolis, I thought it was just something to cheer me up."

184

"No, apparently Maestro Schiff is still intrigued with your concept. If you don't feel up to it, of course, they could go ahead with that Mahler concert without a dancer. But I got the feeling that he really wants you."

"Oh, Ron, when?"

"March fourteenth."

"That's almost exactly a year after my original booking. But March fourteenth is only three months away. I don't know if I can be ready to dance seventy minutes."

"Well, Emily, of course it's up to you. This will be your New York comeback. They need an answer within a day or two."

"Let me think about it, Ron. I'll call you tomorrow." A second chance to do Mahler in Lincoln Center! But seventy minutes. Her body, so battered and chopped, was only beginning to get its strength back.

She called John to talk it over. "It's such a huge thing, and I don't know if I'm ready." She enumerated all the reasons why she should try, take the chance, but she still wasn't sure.

"Emily, you know my basic inclination is to tell you not to do it. But you'll probably fool me again. So, why not?"

In the morning she phoned Ron and told him to ready the contracts with the City Symphony Society.

The Mahler costumes were still in her closet, never unpacked after Indianapolis. Now she took them out, fingering the colorful fabrics, trying them on, noting necessary alterations. She weighed six pounds less, and her torso was a full inch shorter because of the spinal fusion.

She phoned Norman Walker. "Norman, help. My legs are longer."

"Your—what?"

She giggled. "My legs, they're longer now. Or my torso is shorter. I'm not sure which. Anyway, you'll love me even more now. I'm a better instrument. I called you because you have to help me restore the Mahler. I'm going to do it with Maestro Schiff and the City Symphony. My new legs are going back to work."

"You know I'd love to work on the Mahler again, Emily. You and I did some of our best work last year. But what about your back?"

"My back is as strong as it ever was, maybe stronger. It's

185

just different. I can do any movement. I still have technique, but new technique."

"Just think," Walker mused, "a great work, and a new dancer. Different back, new long legs. A showgirl, doing Mahler."

The first day with Norman was exhilarating—hours of sweat and repetitions and an exquisitely tired body when she went to bed. Everything just like the old days, until she awoke the next morning still tired. "I guess I tried to do a little too much yesterday for a lady just out of a hospital bed," she told Walker. The choreographer agreed to work on less strenuous sequences the second day.

"All right," Walker frowned. "Instead of the long diagonal run to down center ending with a jump, give me a shorter run to down left, then reverse the travel with three kicks turns—like this . . . and this . . . and this."

She tried three times to follow his demonstration, then called a halt. "I think I better have a sugar cube," she said. "I need some quick energy."

He answered, "Okay, let's stop. We did some good work today; I like the new sequences."

Before beginning her evening session with Luz Chandler's exercise list, Emily ate four cookies. I've got to find something that'll give me enough energy to get through the list, she thought. I wonder if Ginseng tea might help. I can't remember when I felt this tired.

When Walker arrived for the third afternoon of work, she asked, "What if I took half a Dexamyl before we start? Would you believe? I've still got some from those old company days when I had to drive the bus all night and dance the next day. You're working these legs of mine too hard for such new legs. They feel like I'd been driving all night."

"Maybe so, but they are certainly doing some fine work. Don't take a pill. Let's see how they do with the adagio sequence in the fourth movement. Then I want to get back to where we left off yesterday, the kick turns."

He drove her hard. In the kick turn sequence, he looked at her oddly, then snapped off the music. "Come on, Emily. That's not what I showed you. Not a deep *plié*. You get the momentum for the turn from the *develope* of your *left* leg. And the extension has to be high, *high*."

"All right," she sighed. "I'll try it again." But after one repeat she sagged against the barre. "Can't we take a break now, Norman?"

"Emily, you've never asked to take breaks in all the time I've known you."

"I don't know. I just seem to be so drained these last three days. I've tried everything I've ever heard of to get an energy boost, but nothing seems to work."

"Emily, I've been driving you awfully hard. I know I'm very demanding. But I demand from people according to their ability. Your technique, and my choreography for you, has always been based on your strength. And whether you know it or not, you are stronger now than before."

"Stronger? Tell my new long legs that, Norman."

"Okay, let me see those long legs in some high extensions now. Let's get to the end of the second movement, then we'll quit."

"Could I just mark it, Norman? I *am* awfully tired."

"No. I need your power here. Our point of view is that death is a triumph, right?"

"Right," she replied with a weary smile. "Larger, broader, bigger gestures, higher legs." She willed her body to demonstrate.

"Okay. That's wonderful, Emily. Now do it again. We're going to get it exactly right."

The day was an Olympic marathon to endure. There were moments of high excitement, stimulating discoveries. But this time there was no pleasure in the discoveries. This time there was only numbing exhaustion.

She was so hungry. There must be some food that would replenish her reserves of energy. The foods Dr. Albertson had included on her list just didn't seem to be sufficient for her needs. She decided to experiment, try food with high calorie content, or large amounts of fruit sugar.

Three weeks before the Lincoln Center concert, winding up her evening session in the studio, she felt stomach discomfort. Automatically she checked the clock.

The pains worsened. An Alka-Seltzer was taken. The pains were definitely regular, peristaltic. She pressed a pillow to her stomach; it was swelling again. She knew she must call Albertson again, and get her neighbor to look after David.

At the hospital, she had a barium swallow test and other X rays before Albertson's examination.

He told her, "This time you've got a complete blockage. We can see it on the X rays. I think we're going to have to operate."

"You've told me that without any intestine at all, I'll be confined to bed the rest of my life."

He nodded.

"Let me at least try to wait this one out. How long can you give me before surgery is absolutely necessary?"

"You have about thirteen hours before the onset of gangrene. We can let you go that long without endangering your life. The pain will be severe, but we can't give you any drugs; you must stay awake to help us monitor the condition. If you think you can stand it, I won't schedule the surgery until eleven in the morning."

"I can handle pain. If it hasn't cleared up by morning, I'll sign the surgical permission forms."

The night was as long as Albertson had predicted. Every two minutes peristaltic cramps wrenched at her intestines. Her mind drifted toward unconsciousness. Each time, she fought back.

About 5 A.M. she thought she detected a lessening of the spasms. But they returned, in waves. At 9 A.M., the pain receded again, and this time with steadily decreasing intensity. By 10, she knew she had made it. At the 11 o'clock deadline, Albertson agreed to discharge her.

"Emily, what happened last night could very well happen again. Or it might not. You have what is called the 'Short Bowel Syndrome.' You will have to adjust your entire life, your life-style. The problem is that with only ten percent of your intestine, your body can absorb only ten percent of the food value of what you eat—protein, carbohydrates, calories.

"You will probably suffer from malnutrition the rest of your life. I'll have to do blood and vitamin level tests on a regular basis. And I'm putting you on massive doses of B-12 and B-6. You'll have to come in for an injection at least once a month."

She asked, "Can't I learn to give myself an injection? That's just a matter of poking a needle in the right spot."

188

"Yes. We can teach you how to give yourself an intra-muscular injection."

He continued, "Occasionally, we see patients whose remaining intestine actually stretches as time goes by. But the overall prognosis is for gradual deterioration. Up to now, you have been going on the reserves your body has built up over the years. But the time is coming when your body will require more than it can supply. There is no way we can predict when; all we can predict is that it *will* occur. At that point you will have to begin slowing down, reducing your physical activity." His voice trailed off.

"There's more, isn't there, Doctor?"

"Yes, Emily, there is. You must be prepared for a shortened life expectancy. There is simply no way we can replace your body's steadily depleting stores of essential vitamins and minerals. As your liver works harder because of the deficiency of these elements, it will increase in size. Other likely conditions are gout; a serious form of arthritis; or osteomalacia, the thinning bone syndrome. Eventually, you could be confined to bed."

"Assuming the worst, Dr. Albertson, how long before these conditions start affecting me?"

"Anywhere from a few months to a few years. None of this is certain. It's a rare condition, not one of the well-known diseases like cancer or polio, where great amounts of money are spent for research. It is possible that these particular deteriorative conditions will never manifest themselves, or will do so over such a long period of time that your life expectancy and life-style wouldn't be substantially affected. People react differently to essentially the same conditions."

Emily straightened. "You can't guarantee me anything. That's what you're saying, isn't it, Doctor? I simply have to start working one day at a time—and try to live as normally as I can."

"That's right. There are no guarantees. But we'll work together on this. With your intelligence—"

"And determination," she contributed.

"—and determination," he agreed, "we'll do the best we can."

Emily added, "We'll solve what we can, and learn from the things we can't solve. We'll make a fight of it."

Later in the day, at home, she received a telephone call from her agent.

"Emily, you're not going to believe this, but remember last year when we booked you into Purdue for a road-opening of the Mahler?"

"How could I ever forget?"

"Well, it seems that Purdue wants you back. They've had a dancer cancel for next week, and yesterday they called and asked when you'd be available to dance there. I had them pencil you in conditionally, pending your approval. I figured that you might want to open the Mahler before Lincoln Center. What do you think? I need to call them back and confirm."

"It's almost a year to the day. It's eerie, Ron. But the same reasoning applies as it did a year ago. Before my New York comeback, I need to dance somewhere. Just promise me no car trips to Indianapolis for publicity."

After hanging up the phone, she sat thinking. What an odd, good break. A chance to polish the Mahler off-off-off Broadway. And Purdue again, of all places. I wonder what it is about me and Purdue?

Of course, that means I'll have to push even harder to be ready to dance a week earlier. But that's all right, too. I'll just take each day as it comes; do the best I can.

The weather forecaster on the evening news reported that Indiana's severe winter was continuing. Heavy snow was predicted for the next several days.

Amused, appalled, she could only laugh. Off to Purdue one more time to dance. All right. I'll dance in their damn snow if I have to.

190

14.
Return to Purdue

He looked like a salesman, with his briefcase tucked under his seat and a plastic shirt pocket protector with a company name and six nineteen-cent ball-point pens. He wasn't on the make, but one of those air travelers who must chat compulsively with his seatmate.

"I always hate coming into Lafayette airport," he told Emily. "I fly in here half a dozen times a year and can't ever get over the feeling that this is a dangerous field. They had a bad crash here a couple of years back, you know."

Thanks a lot, friend, she thought, that's all I need to hear. "I travel a lot, too," she answered out loud. "And I've always figured that the easiest way is to consign myself to God and the pilot. There isn't much I can do about it."

Emily craned her neck to look out the window. They were descending through clouds, and occasional glimpses of the ground revealed snowy fields spotted with trees' barren branches. She couldn't avoid a vision of the last time she had entrusted herself to God and the "pilot" and been dealt a black tree trunk alongside a snowy road.

"Excuse me, sir," she said, interrupting the salesman's monologue of disaster. "This conversation makes me very nervous. Can we talk about something else?"

Inside the terminal, Emily was met by two women from the university Public Relations department. The younger woman, a student assistant, took Emily's claim checks and hurried off to collect her luggage. The other simply stood and stared.

"Miss Frankel . . .?"

"Claire . . .?"

They embraced, an island of emotion in a sea of hurrying strangers. Tears marred both women's makeup.

"Oh, Miss Frankel, I wanted to write you a letter or phone, but I was afraid you might hate me," Claire said. "It was all such awful bad luck."

"But it wasn't bad luck, Claire, I've learned so much about myself and my work since then. I understand things I never understood before. That's not bad luck—that's good. I think what happened forced me to face a lot of things within myself I'd been unwilling to face before. And I'm a stronger person since our accident. What's happened to you?"

"I'm remarried now. He's one of the assistant football coaches, a really wonderful man. He really loves me and the kids. And I've had an offer to go to Chicago with one of the big public relations firms."

"You see," Emily continued, "your life changed, too."

"Yes, I guess so. After the accident, I was in the hospital for a month. They had to wire my lower jaw together. I couldn't eat for a long time. And then some plastic surgery. I had a lot of time to think. And I felt so awful about you."

"Well, we're both different people now, and now it's up to us to make the most of our new chance."

As the three women drove out of the airport in the Purdue staff car, the young assistant gunned the engine, fishtailing slightly as they moved onto the snowy highway. Emily turned to the driver. "We have plenty of time, and there's no need to rush. Please slow down." Her voice was quiet, and very firm.

192

Emily turned to Claire. "See? A year ago I couldn't have done that. Now I can even tell taxi drivers to slow down."

It could have been the same room—similar furniture, identical placement of closet, window, and bed. The memories of packing her outfit for the television interview came flooding back. She had been so proud of her Lord & Taylor coat; now it was long consigned to some rag heap in Indianapolis. The bloodstains had been cleaned from her lavender jersey dress, but it didn't fit anymore. All but two of the antique amber beads had been salvaged and the necklace restrung. She had a new traveling outfit, but it could never be as good as her blue corduroy pants and jersey shirt. Like long-ago departed friends she hadn't thought of them for a long time. She moved to the window for a check on the weather. She knew that once again she would see snow.

Emily ate a carton of cottage cheese, one of the few foods that could give her some energy without endangering her intestine. She was hurrying to begin her technical rehearsal.

At the auditorium, her spirit lifted to find the head of the Dance Department at Purdue waiting for her. "At last we're going to get to see you dance. It's a miracle for us that you could come back, and there won't be an empty seat in the house tomorrow night."

He led her to the number one dressing room. On the dresser were vases of flowers—a flood of colors—from students, faculty, hospital staff, strangers who had read about her.

The stage manager pumped her hand, holding out a sheaf of papers in his other hand. "See, I saved your cue sheets from a year ago. And now I get to use them."

Emily laughed at his eagerness. "Well, some of the cues have changed. Let me get into my practice clothes and I'll go over them with you."

"And Miss Frankel? Would you mind autographing them for me? I mean, you're really something special for all of us."

The lighting crew was partly new, and having difficulties with the cues. But it seemed she had only to lift her finger and a crowd of helpers materialized. There were so many people running instruc-

193

tions from her, running questions back, that the tech rehearsal was completed in two hours.

After rehearsal, more than 200 dance and theater students crowded the gym for her master lesson. Many had taken her master lesson the previous year. Afterward, they clustered around her, asking questions, delaying her departure more than an hour. Their lives had been touched by her experience; they seemed to attach an almost mystical significance to her return. They insisted on escorting her back to the hotel, then lingered in the lobby after she retired to her room.

Her telephone was ringing. Dr. Hugh Sam in Indianapolis was on the line.

"Emily! How good to hear your voice. How are you?"

"Dr. Sam, it's good to hear your voice, too. I'm fine. There have been a couple of complications, but I'm dancing again. Isn't that something?"

"I had to show Ed Morrison the notice in the paper before he'd believe me. I'm not normally an 'I-told-you-so' kind of man, but you'd better believe that I told him so, several times."

It seemed she had been laughing the entire afternoon and evening.

"Well, Dr. Sam. I'm not normally an 'I-told-you-so' kind of woman. But—"

"As soon as we saw the notice, Ed and I drove to the Purdue box office to make sure we got the best seats available tomorrow night. And Ed paid for them. He said he so rarely got to see miracles in action that he was willing to pay for the privilege."

"And Mrs. Morgan? How's she doing?"

"Mrs. Morgan left us shortly after you were released. She said you changed her life. She's gone into research work with paraplegics. She wanted to use some of the ideas that the two of you came up with."

Sleep did not come easily. Dreams were a mixture of dark and light; crumpled car, Stryker bed, "paraplegia," plaster cast, flowers, Dr. Sam's smile. Twice she awoke, aware of slight twinges in

194

her stomach—hunger? Or the beginnings of peristaltic pain? She curled around the pillow.

The past year's events came together in a rush. Whooeeee! Just one year ago, I was here preparing for my comeback. Now I've come back, for my comeback, before my comeback in New York. Amused, she tried to verbalize all the comebacks, failed, garbled the words, drifted into sleep.

After a busy morning with reporters and friends, dredging up memories of the past year, her unrested muscles felt curiously leaden. Still, she slipped easily into the comforting ritual—arrive early at the theater, bobby pins, costumes, stage makeup.

She found a quiet corner and stretched out on the floor, needing to rest. But her mind refused to cooperate: I wonder what David is doing right now? What will Dr. Sam think tonight? Forgot to call John last night. My muscles are so sluggish; am I really ready to sustain seventy minutes of dancing? Am I risking failure?

As the curtain went up and the deliberate, tragic grandeur of Mahler's first notes filled the auditorium, she knew that the sense of weight dragging at her limbs all day had not disappeared. Her movement, so lithe and airy in rehearsal, was somewhat mechanical and not inspired. Early in the second movement she missed her mark on the stage floor and the follow-spot lost her, leaving her in near-darkness as the lighting man jerked the spot frantically toward her. She swirled her magnificent robe and nearly toppled one of the props. It had been four years since she had performed on stage and she was not prepared for the brightness of the spotlights coming in at a forty-five-degree angle. In the bright light, she became dizzy, nearly lost her balance.

By the third movement her back was stiffening and her muscles ached. Seventy minutes *is* long. I don't know if I can finish. Thereafter she had no real dramatic concentration and moved only technically through the choreography.

The finish of the dance, when it finally arrived, lacked bravura, and poise. Her mind was blank. She stood exhausted, knowing only that she must bow when the curtain went back up.

195

As she took her first bow to enthusiastic applause, she noticed the head of the Dance Department poised in the wings with an armload of flowers. Oh, no, she thought. A prima ballerina who has just completed a dazzling performance of *Swan Lake* deserves flowers, yes. But not a modern dancer who has just done a poor job of Mahler.

Then he was at her side, handing over the flowers and mumbling words of gratitude and best wishes for her New York performance a week hence. After many obligatory curtain calls she retreated gratefully to her dressing room. There was another assignment—a reception in her honor—before she could rest and think.

Whatever energy remained was consumed in the effort to smile, be gracious and elegant, at the country club party. It was the last place she wanted to be. More people surrounded her, buffeted her with questions, accolades, and memories she'd much rather forget. Finally someone drove her to the hotel where she could at last rest, sleep until the early-morning call for airport departure.

The plane's engines were conducive to thinking. Their drone blotted out conversations and the intrusive little in-flight sounds Emily found so annoying. She was glad to see the Indiana countryside slipping away beneath her.

All right, Emily, she asked herself, what did you learn?

It was an opening on the road. And a road opening is an opportunity to identify problems and work them out. I learned that I wasn't in shape to do a seventy-minute performance. I was tired after the trip from New York. I was nervous because the doctors and a lot of friends were there. There were bad memories to dispose of, and I had been off the stage for four years—I had forgotten technical problems like lights in my eyes.

Should I consider canceling, or at least postponing, Lincoln Center?

No. I can't risk the possibility of losing future bookings. I simply must attack the fears one by one. Identify each fear, and work from moment to moment. Each problem has a solution, so I'll just solve one, then move on to the next. At Lincoln Center, I'll make sure I'm fresh, not tired; I'll concentrate better, won't talk to so many people beforehand; and dammit, I'll anticipate the problems with spotlights.

Above all, I won't be quite so concerned with proving myself to myself.

She hated being late for appointments, and thus arrived a full fifteen minutes ahead of time at Philharmonic Hall. She spent the spare minutes wandering around the magnificient building, found a door that opened into the majestic theater itself, stood at the back and stared down at the huge stage so far away.

Precisely at the tick of the clock of her appointment time, she walked into Maestro Schiff's rehearsal room. Schiff got up from his seat behind the music stand with outstretched hand. "Emily, what an honor it is for me to meet you at last."

"No," she said, "it's my honor." Maestro Schiff was one of the revered figures of the music world. He had a place in history.

And yet, she thought, he looks so human. There were smile lines around his mouth and eyes. He always looked so huge and austere in his pictures on record jackets, yet he was average-size, smaller than she had expected.

"How did it go at Purdue?" he asked.

"Not so well, Maestro. In fact, it would be more accurate to say that it went pretty badly." She related the problems, both human and mechanical, that had plagued her in Indiana.

"For a while, I wished we could cancel or postpone our performance. So many problems, and they all seemed so insurmountable. I really didn't see how I could go through with it."

"Well, I assume that you're here today because you decided not to cancel or postpone," he said.

"Last night in my studio, after I got home, I listened to Mahler again on tape. I heard things I'd never really heard before, or never so clearly. It made me understand much more what I need to do with my performance."

"Emily, I've rehearsed the Fifth Symphony, conducted it, scored it, listened to it, hundreds of times. And I never fail to learn something new about the symphony and about myself. That is the magic of great music."

197

"Mahler triumphed," she continued, "Out of total devastation, he won."

"I don't know how you define your soul, your god, your spirit, Emily. But however you define it, Mahler speaks to you. There is a universality in the man, and both you and I are privileged to be a part of what Mahler created."

Emily knew then she could dance for this man, and do her best.

". . . And you mustn't give too much importance to the problems at Purdue. You were opening on the road. Now you know the problems, and we'll work together on the solutions." He continued, outlining the week's schedule. They would have a tech rehearsal the afternoon of the day before the performance, then a run-through with the orchestra following the tech. There would also be a warm-up rehearsal the day of the performance.

Schiff asked to listen to the performance tape which she had brought with her. "You walk me through your choreography. I need to know your feelings about tempi and dynamics."

"No, Maestro, no. I'll be glad to go through my choreography, but I want you to play the symphony your way. I'll adjust my dynamics to fit your ideas and feelings. The tempo is up to you, and you should have the same freedom to interpret and fulfill the music as you would if it were just a concert with orchestra."

"But Emily, I have worked with dancers before. Tempi are always a problem for dancers. I have to adjust to your choreography—don't I?"

"No. I make the adjustments. My dance is re-created on stage, moment to moment, just as you and the orchestra re-create the symphony each time you perform it—different nuances, subtle alterations in phrasing, all the things you do in a concert performance. That element of spontaneity makes me fly free like a glider. I have controls—the counts, the musical ideas, the choreography—they are my controls. But I don't want to be confined by a preconception of how the music *must* sound, or how the tempo *has* to be."

The conductor answered, "Then that is what makes your dancing unique. I've never worked with anyone like you. But I do know that I'm going to enjoy this experience immensely. We're going to have some fun."

198

"Mitch, can't we re-angle those shin-busters, or make them dimmer?" Emily asked the lighting director. "I'm almost blind out here."

It seemed like she, or somebody else, had stopped the tech rehearsal a hundred times. The members of the orchestra were filling in, noisily taking their seats on the stage, talking in undertones.

The lighting director called back from his rigged board in the center of the orchestra seat section. "Those shin-busters are the only things I've got that'll give you the effect you want. I could try an area spot, but I think we'll lose something. What you've got now looks real good."

"It won't do me much good if I can't dance in it," she laughed. "Maybe you could try a darker blue gel."

"Don," he called to his assistant, "give me blue thirty-six on 12 C and D and 13 C and D."

She repeated the dance sequence, but the new gels were not much help. The intense bright lights, coming at her from the wings, were still blinding. She tried to concentrate on her choreography, but her brain was working on the problem of the lights.

"Mitch, what if we put in a frost? Or, how about another instrument—a thousand-watt Fresnell? What would that give us?"

The director issued the orders, asked her to repeat the dance sequence one more time. "Emily, come out here and take a look for yourself. It's not exactly the effect we talked about this morning, but I like it, maybe even better."

She stepped off the stage and walked down among the empty seats. "I need somebody to stand up there so I can see how they look." She called to Don in the wings: "Would you be me for a minute, please?"

Don, an expert and long-time fixture at Philharmonic Hall, executed an exaggeratedly clumsy *plié*, then lifted his arms and tried a leap, getting perhaps three inches off the floor. "That's enough," Emily called, "no more dancing for you, or Maestro Schiff will put you on in my place tomorrow night."

The new arrangement of lights would work, she saw. The lighting director penciled in the new gels on his copy of her cue sheet. Several members of the stage crew, watching in the wings, rushed to assist her back up onto the stage. "Easy, gentlemen," she bantered. "I may need these arms tomorrow night."

It was like old times. She took special pains to know each member of the crew. She was no prima donna, and they respected her technical knowledge, accepting her as one of their gang. The only worry that she hadn't solved was her extreme fatigue. The endurance she'd gained didn't seem enough to take her through a full day like today.

Near the end of the tech rehearsal she stopped in the middle of a spectacular series of turns. "Do we have a spotting light?"

Philharmonic Hall does not host many dance performances, and Don asked, "What's a spotting light?"

Mitch answered, "A small light in the back of the house so she always knows where front is when she's turning."

Don asked Emily, "Can you use an exit light?"

"No. There are too many of them," Emily said.

Mitch sent two stagehands scurrying into the wings. "Don't worry. We'll rig one for you. If nothing else, we'll have a man standing back there holding a flashlight."

"For seventy minutes? He'll be more tired than I am."

"We'll come up with something, Miss Frankel. It'll be there for you tomorrow night."

Finishing the tech rehearsal, she told Schiff she needed a fifteen-minute break. She knew that rehearsal time for a full symphony orchestra cost six thousand dollars an hour. That'll add fifteen hundred dollars to the theater bill, the new Emily reasoned, but my rest is more important than the cost. After all the money John and I have spent to get me here—hospital, therapy, people, rehearsals—thousands of dollars, it's just not important.

During her break, the stagehands placed her props—tall crosses made of clear plastic rods on globular bases. When she returned to the stage, she made sure that each of her five costume gowns were draped correctly on the crosses, in exactly the right position for her quicksilver onstage costume changes during the dance.

Behind her, the orchestra of 110 pieces was completing its dissonant warm-up. Schiff was on the podium, leafing through his score and chatting with the first violinist. The maestro nodded briskly to Emily. "Ready when you are, Miss Frankel."

200

She moved to her opening position which was marked on the stage with black tape. The musicians' last few warm-up bars faded away, and Schiff tapped the edge of the podium with his baton twice, then raised it. At its down-thrust, the orchestra swept into the thunderous opening chord.

Emily began to dance. Her mind on the lighting problem, she missed a musical cue and went out of the area spot almost immediately. "Maestro, I'm sorry. Can we go back?" The old Emily, good soldier, would have continued without stopping, wanting not to bother the busy musicians. Later, alone, she would have rehearsed the section by herself. But after the Purdue experience, she knew she had to get the music cue and the lighting problem coordinated then and there.

"Certainly." To the orchestra, he announced, "To the top of B, please. Woodwinds? Tympani?"

And on they went. Her mind, trying to hold on to so many factors, was rehearsing, not performing. Her dancing was not crisp, not fluid. It began to feel like Purdue.

But gradually, the grandeur of the music, Schiff's brilliant control, her plan of attack, and what she had learned at Purdue, began to function for her. She allowed herself to work, not try for a "performance" in rehearsal.

Her dancer's mind, in storage so long, began to function smoothly again. It loosened, smoothed out its rhythms, oiled itself. The specifics of choreography began to fall into place—moment by moment, measure by measure. At a certain point, she realized that the rehearsal had become fun. As the negatives dropped away, one by one, she danced cleanly.

When she completed rehearsing curtain calls, Schiff dismissed the orchestra and walked to where she stood in the wings. "Well, Emily, what did you think?"

"It was adequate, good enough for a rehearsal. I learned what I needed."

"We have an afternoon rehearsal penciled in for tomorrow if you want," Schiff said.

"No, I don't need it. I'm concerned about my energy level, and tomorrow I plan to rest, just take a short barre to warm up before the performance. I'm ready for tomorrow, I think."

"I couldn't watch you, of course, but you're right about not rehearsing tomorrow." He started walking away, turned back, added, "Isn't it interesting. In all the years I've conducted, only the very great artists *know* when to stop rehearsing."

Through the morning and the long afternoon, she husbanded her strength. The phone rang several times—her agent about a future booking; John, from the West Coast informing her that he would go straight to Philharmonic Hall when his plane got in; a friend wishing her luck, another wanting tickets. She finally turned on the answering service.

The performance was at eight o'clock. According to her schedule, she should arrive at the theater at four. By two-thirty she was ready to leave the house. Well, she decided, might as well go on and fidget at the theater as fidget around here.

Her stomach felt a little fluttery. A thought of another blockage crossed her mind, and was immediately rejected. A bowl of homemade soup and half a carton of cottage cheese were all she had allowed herself so that her stomach would not swell. No, she thought, it's just performance day nerves, and it's a good feeling. It means I'm keyed up, ready.

Arriving at the theater ahead of everyone but the maintenance crews, she walked slowly, deliberately. She walked out on the stage and stood gazing out at the tiers of empty seats.

Emily had not allowed anyone to tell her of the advance sale. She didn't want to know. A big surge at the box office would have made her nervous; a poor advance would have injured her spirit and confidence. But she couldn't keep from wondering how many of those seats will be filled tonight? And what will they see? A dancer who could have been great but was destroyed by fate and her own inability to see herself clearly? Or will they see a dancer who has passed the toughest tests of her life, and has made herself more than what she was before? No, I learned not to think that way when I was at Purdue. Tonight's just one performance. After tonight, no matter how it goes, I have more to do.

There were bookings—a tour of South America and Africa and Australia. And she would keep on dancing because it was good to work, because her dancing required the ultimate in concentration,

202

intellect, nerve, and artistry. Never again would she dance in the grip of a compulsive childhood dream.

In old practice clothes—wool tights, baggy rubber sweat pants, and a shapeless wool sweater—she started her performance routine. To the ticks of her silver hand metronome, she went through a careful series of limbering-up exercises. To recorded instructions on a cassette tape, she took a short barre. She was not distracted by the stagehands beginning to straggle in.

In the guest performer's dressing room, the "star"location immediately adjacent to Schiff's, she began to lay out each item she would need for the night's performance. The elements of her stage makeup—base, eye-liner, powder, pale lipstick—were aligned in order of usage. Next came a neat row of bobby pins and hairpins. There was comfort in the old ritual. Then small pads for her toe joints and Elmer's Glue for the heels of her shoes.

She stretched out on the hard floor, mentally signaling each muscle to relax, one by one. People were starting to poke their heads into her dressing room, wishing her luck, asking last-minute questions, giving information.

She closed the door, rested fifteen minutes more, then put on her makeup. Donning her coat, she found an emergency exit and walked outside, under the clear winter New York sky.

For several minutes, she simply stood, gazing up. Gradually the city sounds faded from her perception. The backstage clamor was forgotten, even thoughts of home and husband and son. Her thoughts moved inward. She was going into her "zeroed zone," away from all of the world's logic and concerns.

She blew a kiss to the north, south, east, and west. She whispered. "Okay God, here we are, under this sky, alone, about to dance. When I was a child, Daddy always said you didn't exist." She smiled to herself, continued, "But I guess, for me, you exist in some way that I don't quite understand, but accept, because here I am 'phoning' you again.

"A lot of things have happened to me, and I haven't 'called' you. This is awfully big for me, tonight. Soon I'll be all alone on the stage, and that's my work—it's entirely up to me. And that's okay, too, because I'm ready. Whatever happens, I'll go on with my work."

She thought a moment, then added, "But whoever you

are, when I was a child, I promised you I would dance until death do us part. I've come close to death, and it hasn't parted us yet, so I guess you and I both want me to dance well tonight. I guess that's why I'm calling—to say thanks."

She was turning back to the door when something caught her attention, breaking the spell. The sidewalk beyond the end of the little alley in which she was standing was filled with a double line of people moving slowly. That's strange, she thought, I wonder what's going on?

Back inside, she walked across to the stage door and peeked outside again. To one side, a mob milled in front of the box office. People were clutching tickets, others urging those in front to hurry so they could get their turn at the window. Others waved excited arms in the air. A long line of limousines parked at the curb lent the appearance of a major Broadway opening night.

In the other direction, the double line of people extended to the corner, then bent on around. Police barricades maintained order.

She ducked back inside, queried a stagehand, "How many people are out there?"

"Thousands, Miss Frankel. The line for tickets goes all the way around the block."

My goodness, she thought, must be Maestro Schiff conducting the City Symphony in Mahler's Fifth. I understand they had quite a house last night. Mahler's becoming quite a cult figure these days.

"Don't want to make you nervous or anything, Miss Frankel," the stagehand continued, "but they're here to see you. That's what I hear."

Emily pulled on her flesh-colored body suit, smoothing the tight-knit fabric to every line of her slender body. The effect was startling—nudity without exposure. She wrapped the small foam pads to the balls of her feet to support the painful bone-on-bone structure. Next, she applied glue to the heels and soles of her feet, then put on her dance slippers, wiggling her feet until they were secure, pressing on the glued areas so that her shoes would be as firmly connected to her feet as her own skin. The hairdresser entered and went to work on the glamorous styling so necessary to the opening effect of her first costume.

The stage manager knocked and entered. "Hi, Miss Frankel. How are you feeling?"

"Fine, thanks. Ready for the performance."

"So is everybody out here. We've got the best house we've had this whole concert series. Even the crew's keyed up. You've got all the critics here, too."

"All? What do you mean?"

"The music critics, of course. And some dance critics, too, and a couple of the drama critics. Miss Frankel, this is a big event."

"Yes," she chuckled. "It's going to be an interesting evening, I think. Fun."

He added, "Maestro Schiff sends good luck wishes. I've got stacks of flowers outside. We'll bring them in while you're on stage."

At the five-minute call, she walked out to the wings. Members of the orchestra glanced in her direction, smiled in welcome. Schiff nodded imperceptibly. She looked over her crosses, determined that they were in the proper locations and the gowns draped correctly. The stage manager left his post by the light board and walked to her side. "We've got the 'spotting light' rigged on the back wall, directly in the middle, just under the mezzanine. When the house lights go down, you'll be able to see it."

"Thank you."

She simply stood, her mind empty of specific thoughts. Her muscles quietly awaited her signal to move. As the house lights went down, she went to her place on the stage, marked by the small piece of tape. The rustling and whispered conversation in the audience dwindled to silence. She saw the spotting light.

Suddenly, the pure white shaft of a spotlight pinned her to the stage. There was a burst of welcoming applause. She stood taut, proud, her pale face haughty, eyes staring out over the heads of the audience. She was tall, huge, dominating the stage.

Schiff lifted his baton, slashed downward, and the first notes of Mahler's Fifth began.

As if of their own volition, her feet began to move, her arms to raise, her fingers to gesture, her head to turn. Her body

205

followed into the powerful striding, heavy *chassé plié* that opened the first movement. And then she was whirling, swirling off her cloak, running free with the musical rhythms, flickering like a magical impulse of light. Enchanting, entrancing, her slender frame filled the stage with movement.

She was not dancing for Miss Charlotte, Charles Weidman, her father or mother, or Dr. Sam, or other dancers, or critics, or gods, but simply for the music itself. She was power, strength, grief and joy and agony, sanguine grace, dominance.

Her feet, leaving the floor in a series of light jumps, seemed to release her from the forces of gravity. Higher and higher she went until she soared from the stage in a magnificent leap. Zephyr flew. The notes of the music fluttered in her wake, sailing after the eloquent torso, arms, fingers.

She had dreaded the four revolutions of the off-balance, dangerous pirouette ending the first movement, and considered making it a safe three. Now she made it five turns, spinning flawlessly, effortlessly, joyously.

She was a part of the orchestra. The conductor sensed her inspiration, caught it, and drove the orchestra past its peak. Emily felt every nuance, anticipating and attacking each phrase, each chord, each note.

When it was over, seventy minutes after the opening white spot had pinned her, she stood still at center stage, regal, calm in the knowledge that she had truly danced.

There was silence from the packed theater.

Then she heard it begin—hands clapping, thousands of hands transmitting pleasure and happiness and tribute. She knew from the sound that people were rising to their feet, dropping programs and gloves and coats as they rose, engulfing her with an avalanche of praise.

She bowed low, a long sweeping gesture of acknowledgment, then stepped to the side and gestured back at the conductor. He bowed in turn, beckoned his Concert Master to rise, then the entire orchestra.

She exited, donned a white satin robe designed for curtain calls. The conductor was waving her back onstage.

She bowed again, the physical force of the applause and bravas assaulting her ears.

206

It began then, in the far reaches of the balcony, a primitive roar as if a subway train was passing beneath the building. It spread down through the tiers of the mezzanine, was picked up at the rear of the orchestra seats, rolling steadily forward to the front rows—a thumping rhythm that overpowered even the sound of applause. For a moment, Emily was frightened until she recognized the stamping of feet, in mighty unison, a thunder that seemed to shake the building. Again she gestured to Maestro Schiff, and noticed that he and the orchestra were standing and applauding her.

A new sound began in the balcony. It was a chant now, yelled in the rhythm of the stamping feet, backed by the rhythmic clapping of hands. As each row of people heard tumult behind them, they picked it up and passed it on.

"Frank-el, Frank-el, Frank-el . . ." It continued, rising in tempo and volume.

She smiled, she waved, she bowed and bowed and bowed. She tried to escape to the wings, but they demanded she stay and receive their acclaim. In the spillover of light from the stage, she saw John in the second row, standing with the others. He was laughing and crying. My big John, she thought in wonderment, standing there crying.

"Frank-el, Frank-el, Frank-el . . ."

Epilogue

The lights burn late in the window of the little office on the third floor of Dancehouse. Harriet Schaeffer is hard at work. The small, fine-boned, pale, red-headed woman moves purposefully from automatic typewriter to complex accounting books to filing cabinets to electric typewriter. In the large studio beyond music is playing—a symphony. Occasionally she makes pencil notes after a particular passage.

There are scripts to update, tax reports to prepare, a mailing to get out, choreographic notes to record. The telephone interrupts often, and the intercom crackles messages from the family's quarters upstairs. Decisions are being made.

Energy and enthusiasm fill the small office, along with a quantity of sophisticated equipment necessary to a diversified career in the theater. Around her are two automatic typewriters, the latest model electric typewriter, two desks, telephones and recorded answering-service machines, a computerized adding machine, a wooden filing cabinet, a steel filing cabinet. Every piece of equipment comes into use at least once during the evening. Overhead are shelves for accounting books and supplies, road maps, and a crawl space crammed with costumes and props.

Occasionally she refers to her bulletin wall. It is a current business reference studded with a variety of pins and tacks securing directories, maps, choreography notes, poems, addresses, bills, warranties, costume swatches, odd scraps of reminders. Despite the apparent disorder, everything is organized, compact and efficient. Ask her a question, and the woman can put her finger on an answering document in seconds.

Emily completes a script revision, decides the next day's rehearsal must be moved up an hour, and instructs Harriet to phone cast members notifying them of the change. Emily hates to talk on the telephone.

Harriet is too busy for social conversation, but Emily stops for a moment and says, "I'm a closet writer," with a shy smile.

While this book was being written, Emily wrote, mounted, and performed in three productions:

Kings, three stories based on Greek mythology, had a limited run on Broadway. For the first drama, *Oedipus,* starring John Cullum in the title role, Emily created an original musical score and directed the cast. John wrote the script. The second piece, *Medea,* a ballet drama from Emily's repertory, included her son in the cast. In the final number, *Theseus and Hippolyta,* John acted the role of the Greek king Theseus, and Emily danced the role of the Queen of the Amazons. She wrote the script based on the Mary Renault book, *The Bull From the Sea.*

For *Zinnia,* which ran for several months off-Broadway, Emily wrote the play, and choreographed and danced the title role to Mahler's Tenth (Unfinished) Symphony. Husband John directed.

A new project, *People in Show Business Make Long Good-byes,* was being readied for studio showcase performances as this book went to press. In this project, Emily performs as an actress; again, John is the director.

Now she is wondering whether to remain in the closet as a writer, or come out. "I came out of the closet for *Zinnia,*" she explains. "But I discovered that it is very complicated to perform in one's own play. And it confuses people. Perhaps I should just stay in the closet from now on and let Harriet have the credit."

Since the accident, in addition to her writing, Emily has toured the world dancing with symphony orchestras, continued dancing with major civic symphony orchestras in this country, and was a starring dancer and choreographer at the Spoleto Festival of Two Worlds. She also found time to direct a children's opera, *Babar the Elephant*, at Lincoln Center.

"Slowed down." She repeats, incredulously, "If anything, I'm doing more and working harder than at any other time in my life." The question of her medical problems, the effects of her accident, is raised. Doesn't she have problems maintaining her energy? What about those feet the doctors told her so long ago were totally unsuited to dancing?

"Yes, there are problems. I have problems with energy. And of course there's pain. My feet hurt most of the time."

But if your feet hurt, how can you dance?

"It's a matter of understanding the causes of the pain. The mystery of pain is what we fear. Once we understand *why* something hurts, we can deal with it. For my feet, I take some medication in the morning, then take my barre. I warm up the feet slowly, and once I break through the pain barrier, I can work."

She glances at the clock, hurries upstairs to supervise her son's homework responsibilities.

There have been many changes in the building since the little girl carried her orange crates up the stairs.

The third floor she has just left is the working space. In addition to Emily's office, there is an office for John, two dressing rooms, a hall lined with steel shelves containing the paraphernalia of her work—makeup, slides, press materials, publicity photos—office supplies, and John's assortment of tools. These areas serve as support facilities for the studio—an enormous, unobstructed room all in white, mirrors lining the length of one wall, a barre lining the other. Above the barre are cabinets for the record collection. The studio's ceiling is dotted with flood lights, shining down on equipment that includes a grand piano, a sound system worthy of a professional recording studio, and video tape equipment with remote connections to the family's television sets upstairs. Everything is on wheels, and electrical outlets line the baseboards, giving Emily maximum mobility and efficiency of operation.

Upstairs, the changes are even more dramatic—an eclectic loft home replacing the old Orange Palace.

What was once living quarters is now the study and David's bedroom, the latter done in green and blue with a psychedelic Emily-painted ceiling. The room is filled with bunk bed, and built-in desk, and David's electronic sound equipment. The study, an old-fashioned room in dark red and brown tones, contains stereo sound equipment, a pool table lighted by a Tiffany lamp, floor-to-ceiling bookshelves and Emily's mural walls. The only furniture is a couch that wraps around two sides of the room.

Separating that area of the house from the domestic center is the "living wall." Three tanks of tropical fish appear suspended because of the cantilevered arrangement of Plexiglas shelves that Emily designed. There is also an antique brass bird cage with its resident, a large white pigeon.

The domestic center, kitchen and dining room, is a model of streamlined efficiency. An interior wall with gold stained-glass window and open pass-through—another Emily idea—divides the space lengthwise. On one side is the stark black-and-white dining area with a wall of pleated black velvet. The kitchen side, in tones of bright orange, white, and chocolate, requires only a few steps from food storage cabinets to cooking and washing site to serving area. Tying the domestic center together is a giant free-form white table curling from the kitchen through the wall to the dining space.

A white S-curved wall opens through a keyhole doorway and display windows to the Green Room. You guessed it—Emily designed the wall. The Green Room is decorated as an old-fashioned summer porch with green floor and ceiling, white walls, and white wicker furniture. The skylight which once confined the Dance Drama Duo's lifts is now a greenhouse of plants large and small. This area of the house was the original dance studio, and the mirror walls are now stuccoed in a design resembling the rocky bed of a mountain stream.

Finally, through white beaded curtains, is the master bedroom suite. The motif is a cozy Maine attic with the building's original brick walls and dark wood beams exposed. The color scheme is warm, dark, soft brown.

The people around Emily have changed as well. John's career has rocketed in the Broadway world, bringing him two Tony awards, his name above the title, and the reputation as Broadway's

212

top musical comedy actor. David is a twelve-year-old boy with a bright, inquisitive mind currently investigating electronic music and composing on his synthesizer. He has worked so hard on his tennis game that he is entering New York area tournaments.

Outwardly, Emily is still the dedicated worker—taking her daily barre, doing concert bookings, touring, choreographing for dance companies, rehearsing, writing, and composing. But there is a significant difference. "The accident gave me new problems, as any major change in one's life does, and additional factors to be handled. It taught me to understand myself better, physically and mentally. I'm more focused now."

Oh, yes, one more thing—Zephyr is gone. There is only Emily Frankel. That is sufficient.